D0540761

# Healthy Cooking for Diabetics

# Healthy Cooking for Diabetics

# Contents

Introduction 5

Breakfasts 18

Lunches 46

Dinners 78

Sides and snacks 110

Baking and desserts 134

Index 158

# Introduction

If you have been diagnosed with diabetes – or someone close to you has – it can be extremely dismaying. However, major advances in our understanding of this condition and in its treatment and management mean that today 'everything is possible' in life, even if you are diabetic. While it is important to keep a careful eye on your food intake – especially for sufferers of Type 1 diabetes and others who need to use insulin – there truly is still a whole world of delicious food out there for you to enjoy.

In recent years, health professionals have realised that it is not necessary for the diabetic to eat a very restricted diet, nor is it necessary for them to forego eating the same meals as the rest of their family and friends. The diet suitable for the majority of diabetics is one that everyone can enjoy – a healthy, nutritious diet with no food groups excluded and with no obscure, hard-to-find ingredients. The diabetic diet is, in fact, a great way to eat for anyone who values their health – and their taste buds! Just a glance through these pages will give you a taste of the fantastic recipes that you, your friends and your family can feast on.

# Types of diabetes

## *Type 1 diabetes*

Type 1 diabetes is most commonly diagnosed in childhood (and used to be known as 'juvenile diabetes' for that reason) but it can actually begin at any age. It is also called 'insulin-dependent diabetes' because for those with Type 1 diabetes insulin is vital in its management.

Insulin is a hormone that helps your body use the glucose your body gets through the food you eat, providing you with energy. In Type 1 diabetes, the body is unable to produce any insulin so glucose builds up in the blood. Meanwhile, your body begins to look for sources of energy elsewhere and breaks down its fat stores or the proteins in your muscles – hence why sufferers can lose weight.

The causes are still being researched, but Type 1 diabetes may be triggered by viruses or bacterial infections. Apart from weight loss, other usual symptoms include having to urinate more frequently (as the body is trying to flush out the unused/surplus glucose) and extreme tiredness. Currently, there is no cure for Type 1 diabetes but it can be treated and managed using insulin injections or an insulin pump in conjunction with a healthy lifestyle and diet.

## *Type 2 diabetes*

Accounting for 90 per cent of diabetes cases, Type 2 diabetes is the most common type of diabetes. It develops when the body doesn't produce enough insulin, or when the insulin that is produced doesn't work properly (called 'insulin resistance').

Type 2 diabetes used to be called 'midlife onset diabetes' because it does indeed affect a large number of people in midlife, but there are growing numbers of younger sufferers and many experts link this surge to an increase in obesity and inactivity. High blood pressure and a large waist circumference (because fat stored around the midriff, known as 'visceral fat', appears to decrease insulin sensitivity and increase insulin resistance) are two risk factors.

Type 2 diabetes can cause serious long-term health problems so it is important to be diagnosed early and to control your blood glucose levels in order to prevent these complications. Blood sugar levels may be controlled with a healthy diet, weight loss if necessary and increased physical activity, although sometimes treatment with medication and/or insulin is also needed.

## *Gestational diabetes*

This type of diabetes occurs for the first time in women during pregnancy and, in most cases, disappears after pregnancy is over. The cause is usually that the pregnant woman has a much higher than normal level of glucose in her blood and can't produce enough insulin to make her body able to use it all. It can be managed/treated in a similar way to Type 2 diabetes.

# What is a healthy diet for diabetics?

A healthy diet is important for everyone but it is especially important for diabetics. Across the world over the past 60 or so years, health professionals and researchers have wavered somewhat about what constitutes the best diet for diabetics. A recent report by the American Diabetes Association stated 'there is one certainty about diet and diabetes – there is no one diet that is right for all'.

Of course, research into the 'best' diet for diabetics is still ongoing and there are one or two areas that may turn out to be exciting. For example, there has been much debate in the past few years about higher-protein, moderate-carbohydrate diets. Some research shows that such a diet can help control blood insulin even better than the higher-carbohydrate one usually recommended, and is better in helping with weight loss and weight control. There is also interest in a diet high in 'resistant starch' – a type of dietary fibre naturally found in many carbohydrate-rich foods, such as potatoes, grains, and beans, particularly when these foods are cooked and then cooled. It gets its name because it 'resists' digestion, and it appears to increase the body's ability to burn fat, reduce overall hunger and improve blood sugar control.

At the present time, however, the recommendations given by leading diabetes organisations for how diabetics should eat are strikingly similar to the guidelines that non-diabetics are often asked to follow for a generally healthy diet. For a start, we all need a good balance of the major nutrients ('macronutrients') – carbohydrates, fats and protein – in our diets.

### *Carbohydrates*

Carbohydrates are our body's main energy source. Carbohydrates – including both starches and sugars – easily convert into glucose within the digestive system, which is then used to provide us with the energy we need in our daily lives. Some good sources of carbohydrates for diabetics include pulses (such as beans, peas and lentils), wholegrains (such as oats, barley, rye, spelt, rice and wheat) and starchy vegetables (including root vegetables) and whole fruits, particularly those with a lower glycaemic index (see panel opposite). It is important to eat enough – but not too many – carbohydrates as they can't be stored in the body as they are but are instead converted into body fat.

### *Fats*

Fats have many roles within the body and the fats we eat in food are broken down into fatty acids of many different types. These help proteins to do their work, assist our bodies in storing and using certain vitamins, and also aid in the control of growth, immune function, reproduction and metabolism.

Although fat is energy dense and easily stored in the body, there is no need for diabetics to avoid eating fat. Indeed some fats – monounsaturated fats (found in quantity in foods like olive oil, avocados, and some nuts and seeds) and certain types of polyunsaturated fats (found in quantity in foods like oily fish, some nuts and seeds, and plant oils) have positive health benefits for everyone, including diabetics. Saturated fats (found in quantity in foods like full-fat dairy produce, fatty cuts of meat, and many highly processed foods, such as pastries, desserts, cakes and biscuits) are less beneficial and, if eaten in quantity, may increase the risk of health problems, including cardiovascular disease. Hydrogenated fats – fats altered in the manufacturing process to harden them – are believed to be even worse for the health than saturated fats and are best avoided, if possible. Thankfully, these fats are slowly being phased out from food manufacture so it is becoming easier to find products free from hydrogenated fats.

### *Protein*

Like fats, protein has many roles to play – our connective tissue, skin, hair and muscles are all made up of protein and without it we couldn't maintain our muscle mass, our vital organs and our skin, or build new cells. Protein plays a crucial role in all of our cells, including our DNA, hormones and enzymes. All these functions need us to eat protein regularly. A diet containing adequate protein is equally important to diabetics as it is to non-diabetics, as long as there is a balance of sources – not relying on too much red meat, for example. Good protein sources for diabetics include fish, poultry, small amounts of lean red meat, pulses, eggs, reduced-fat dairy produce, and nuts and seeds.

## The glycaemic index

The glycaemic index is a ranking of all carbohydrate foods according to the rate at which the starches and sugars they contain are absorbed into the body and get into the bloodstream as blood glucose. A ranking of 100 is the highest, while a ranking of 1 is the lowest. Foods with a high GI (over 70) are the quickest to be absorbed and foods with a low GI (55 or under) are the slowest to be absorbed. Medium GI foods have a rating of 56 to 69. The glycaemic index was originally devised in the 1980s to help diabetics to make wise food choices, and thus help them to control their blood sugars and medications.

In practice, however, most people eat or drink high-carbohydrate, high-GI foods along with other foods. For example, you may have boiled potatoes with fish, or pasta with a cheese and ham sauce. The fat and protein accompanying your carbohydrate food has the effect of reducing the 'spike' effect. As a result, it may be important for diabetics to eat carbohydrate foods – particularly those at the high end of the GI ranking – with proteins and fats to minimise this effect. (The glycaemic index lists only carbohydrate foods; there is no GI ranking for proteins and fats.) Most studies have also shown that, compared to low-GI meals, high-GI meals lead to lower satiety, increased hunger levels or increased food intake, so eating more low-GI foods can be useful for weight loss diets. Finally, the glycaemic effect of a food also depends on how much of it you eat. The glycaemic load (GL) of a food or meal calculates the effect by using a formula based on the weights of carbohydrate foods consumed as well as their theoretical GI value.

**High-GI foods include:** sugar of all types, watermelon, bananas, mashed potatoes, white bread and cornflakes.

**Medium-GI foods include:** sweet potatoes, boiled potatoes, pasta, sweetcorn, oatmeal, wholegrain bread, oranges, grapes and figs.

**Low-GI foods include:** lentils, kidney beans, chickpeas, baked beans, whole barley, apples, dried apricots, plums, cherries, natural yogurt and milk.

### *Foods to avoid*

So is there any type of food that diabetics should avoid? The answer to that question is 'no', or rather, 'not completely'. Diabetes organisations recommend keeping your **saturated fat** intake low, but there are no current guidelines on maximum intake specific to diabetics. Because of the link between cardiovascular disease, high blood pressure and diabetes, it is also wise to limit your **salt** intake to a maximum of 6 grams a day – not just of added salt but also of high-salt foods, such as bacon and ham, packet soups, sauces and stock cubes, and takeaway food. Moderate amounts of **alcohol** – no more than one small alcoholic drink a day for women and two for men – are fine (but do consult your doctor first). Intake of **carbohydrates** in their simple, highly processed forms (such as sugar, white flour, white pasta, white rice and goodies like commercial pastries, cakes and biscuits) needs to be watched. This is especially important if you are overweight because these types of foods tend to be low in nutrients and are often high in calories and sometimes fat.

# Sugar – what you need to know

Dietitians divide the sugars that we eat into two different types – intrinsic (the sugars that form a natural part of the structure of a food, as in fruits, for example) and extrinsic (those that are not a natural part of a food and instead are added in the manufacturing process or at the table). Milk contains an extrinsic sugar, lactose, which is not normally grouped with the extrinsic sugars. Extrinsic sugars may also be referred to as 'free sugars'.

* **High intrinsic sugar** foods include many fruits, especially dried and tropical fruits, and a surprising number of vegetables, such as beetroot, carrots, sweetcorn, sweet peppers, potatoes, peas, onions and parsnips. However, it is important not to avoid all fruits and vegetables containing sugar because they provide a range of important nutrients, as well as dietary fibre and health-promoting plant compounds.

* **High or very high extrinsic sugar** foods include confectionery, cakes, desserts, soft drinks and biscuits, as well as some breakfast cereals and bars, low-fat fruit yogurts and some alcoholic drinks, such as sweet cider and sweet wine.

So if you are cutting back on sugar, should you use sugar substitutes instead? There are many different types:

* **Natural sugar alternatives** – these include maple syrup, agave nectar, date syrup and rice malt syrup and are useful as an occasional, and often flavoursome, alternative to sugar. They have similar calorie contents to sugar but tend to be higher in fructose (fruit sugar). The American Diabetes Association says agave nectar and other natural sweeteners should be limited in a diabetic diet and the consensus seems to be that they offer little benefit over sugar.

* **Artificial sweeteners** – these include all zero-calorie and very low-calorie sugar substitutes, such as aspartame, saccharin, acesulfame K and sucralose. All these have been passed as safe in the EU and USA and don't affect the blood sugars. However, some people find they leave an aftertaste or simply do not taste as good as sugar.

* **Sugar alcohols** – these products include mannitol, sorbitol, erythritol and xylitol and contain fewer calories than sugar – around half to a third less. Sugar alcohols can cause diarrhoea, bloating and weight gain if consumed in large quantities, and do affect blood sugars.

* **Stevia** – a unique sweetener, stevia is made with an approved extract from a plant, *Stevia rebaudiana*, native to South America. Recent research shows it may help to reduce high blood pressure, maintain constant blood sugar levels and minimise liver and kidney damage in diabetics. There are many different brands and varieties of stevia sweetener available – we've used both stevia granules (the virtually calorie-free version that can be used to replace sugar teaspoon for teaspoon) and stevia liquid.

### *Reading labels*

When you buy processed foods, be aware that sugar can be disguised in the ingredients labels in a variety of different names. All the following are basically types of sugar: *cane sugar, corn sweetener, corn syrup, corn syrup solids, dextrose, fructose, fruit juice concentrates, honey, lactose, maltose, malt syrup* and *maple syrup.*

# Healthy eating for diabetics – top ten tips

### *1. Choose a wide variety of foods*

This will help to ensure you get all the nutrients that your body needs in a good balance.

### *2. Try to eat naturally*

Keep highly processed items, such as shop-bought cakes, pies, biscuits and so on, for occasional consumption. Eating a natural diet is an easy way to reduce your intake of saturated and hydrogenated fats, salt and sugar.

### *3. Choose fruit for a sweet taste*

For those with a sweet tooth, low-GI fresh fruits, such as cherries, plums, apples and peaches, are an ideal easy dessert – their fibre content slows down insulin release.

### *4. Limit soft drinks and juices*

High-sugar drinks, such as colas, lemonade and fruit juice, are digested very quickly and can provoke high blood sugar.

### *5. Choose water*

The best drinks to choose are water or tea/coffee, with a little skimmed or semi-skimmed milk if liked, all of which have minimal effect on blood sugars.

### *6. Eat regularly*

This is especially important for Type 1 diabetics and helps to prevent hypoglycaemia (low blood sugar). Eating regularly also helps to avoid hunger pangs and may help to control weight.

### *7. Think 'good' carbohydrates every day*

Eat carbohydrates with a high fibre content and/or a low GI and/or a high content of resistant starch (see page 7) – they can also be a great source of nutrients.

### *8. Make your plates colourful*

Foods that are green, orange, yellow, red or purple, for example, tend to contain high levels of antioxidant compounds, which can help to prevent diabetes-related diseases, such as cardiovascular disease.

### *9. Take healthy snacks with you*

When out and about, carry portable snacks, such as nuts mixed with a few ready-to-eat dried apricots and raisins; ideal for short-term and long-term energy and stable blood sugars.

### *10. Take time over your food*

Don't forget to enjoy preparing your food and eating it. Food is a pleasure to be savoured and can even help you to reverse your diabetes symptoms.

# Daily nutritional guidelines

The recipes in this book have been developed to fit into what is generally considered to be a healthy diet for both diabetics and non-diabetics, while also focusing on the 'good' carbohydrates and keeping added (extrinsic) sugar to a minimum. We have assumed that 50 per cent of total daily calories will come from carbohydrates (to consist of mainly low-GI carbohydrates high in fibre and/or resistant starch); a maximum of 30 per cent from fat (of which no more than a third should be saturated fat), and 20 per cent from protein (which should be eaten mostly in the form of the proteins described on page 8 as being best for diabetics). However, protein intake is flexible and could vary between 10 per cent and 25 per cent depending on individual preference (adjusting proportions of carbohydrates/fat accordingly). Advice on sugar intake varies across the world, but we have based our guidelines on a total sugar intake equivalent to or less than 10 per cent of daily calories, most of which should come from intrinsic sugars.

The table below shows how this advice translates into a nutritional breakdown for each meal of the day. The information in this table is based on a daily intake of 2,000 calories, which is suitable for weight maintenance of an average woman.

| | Calories (kCal) | Maximum carbs | Maximum total sugars | of which extrinsic sugars | Maximum total fat | of which maximum saturated fats | Protein |
|---|---|---|---|---|---|---|---|
| Breakfast | 400 | 53 g | 10 g | 5 g | 13 g | 4.5 g | 10–25 g |
| Lunch | 500 | 67 g | 10 g | 0 g | 17 g | 5.5 g | 12.5–31 g |
| Dinner | 600 | 80 g | 10 g | 0 g | 20 g | 6.5 g | 15–38 g |
| Snack or side | 200 | 27 g | 5 g | 0 g | 7 g | 2 g | 5–12.5 g |
| Dessert or bake | 200 | 27 g | 10 g | 5 g | 7 g | 2 g | 5–12.5 g |
| Milk allowance (100 ml/3½ fl oz semi-skimmed milk) | 50 | 5 g | 5 g | 0 g | 2 g | 1.2 g | 3.3 g |
| Daily total | 1,950* | 259 g | 50 g | 10 g | 66 g | 21.7 g | 50.8–122.3 g |

* With an additional maximum 50 calories for 'free' extras, such as green vegetables and salad, taking total to 2,000 calories

The above values are intended as a guideline only. Although people with Type 2 diabetes do not need to work out every gram of carbohydrate or sugar in every meal, those with Type 1 diabetes will need to match their insulin intake with their carbohydrate intake. It is important that all individuals consult the healthcare practitioner or team monitoring their diabetes before making any dietary changes.

In order to ensure a good variety of recipes in this book, the exact nutritional breakdowns of the individual recipes vary in terms of the proportions of macronutrients they contain. It is therefore important to balance these across the day's eating. So, for example, if you choose a low-protein (or low-carbohydrate) lunch, you should then pick a higher-protein (or high-carbohydrate) dinner and vice versa.

In the pages that follow, we give two seven-day diet plans as examples of how to build a day's healthy eating based on the recipes in this book. Plan 1 is designed to help those with a healthy body weight maintain that weight, whilst Plan 2 targets weight loss. According to the International Diabetes Federation, 80 per cent of the world's Type 2 diabetics are overweight or obese at the time of diagnosis. Reducing body weight by just 5–10 per cent can help to slow or stop the progress of Type 2 diabetes, so losing weight is a positive step that sufferers can take to manage their condition.

# Diet plans

## Plan 1: **Weight maintenance**

* **Calorie goal:** approximately 2,000 calories a day (based on average adult woman). Men should aim for approximately 2,500 calories a day and therefore increase portion sizes throughout by 25 per cent.

* **Consume freely:** leafy green vegetables and salad vegetables (such as lettuce, cucumber, radish and celery), fresh herbs and spices, lemon juice and vinegar.

* **To drink:** water and/or tea/coffee (with milk from allowance).

* **Milk allowance:** 100 ml/3½ fl oz semi-skimmed milk (50 calories) for use in tea and coffee, or as you like. (Daily totals all include milk allowance.)

* **Alcohol:** no more than one small alcoholic drink a day for women and two for men (on consultation with your healthcare practitioner). Calories to be taken from dessert allowance.

| | Recipe/Food | Calories |
|---|---|---|
| **Day one** | **Total (including milk allowance)** | **1,931** |
| Breakfast | *Coconut and blackberry porridge* (p.21) | 322 |
| Mid-morning snack | *Nut and seed bar* (p.141) | 213 |
| | 1 satsuma | 40 |
| Lunch | *Aubergine paprika salad* (p.68) | 475 |
| | 1 apple | 60 |
| Dinner | *Chicken escalopes with cherry tomatoes* (p.88) | 342 |
| | *Sweet potato fries* (p.112) | 183 |
| Dessert | *Indivdual plum and rhubarb crumble* (p.150) | 208 |
| | 50 g/1¾ oz full-fat Greek-style yogurt | 38 |
| **Day two** | **Total (including milk allowance)** | **1,991** |
| Breakfast | *Eggs Benedict with asparagus and Parma ham* (p.36) | 342 |
| | 1 kiwi fruit | 30 |
| Mid-morning snack | 1 heaped tbsp *Home-made cashew nut butter* (p.128) | 153 |
| | 2 dark rye crispbreads | 68 |
| Lunch | 125 g/4½ oz smoked salmon | 275 |
| | 1 slice *Pumpernickel bread* (p.137) | 135 |
| | 2 tsp dill mustard sauce | 46 |
| Dinner | *Spaghetti and meatballs* (p.83) | 585 |
| | 30 g/1 oz Parmesan cheese shavings | 116 |
| | Large mixed leaf salad with 2 tsp vinaigrette dressing | 40 |
| Dessert | *Vanilla custard cup with raspberry coulis* (p.154) | 151 |
| **Day three** | **Total (including milk allowance)** | **1,997** |
| Breakfast | *Healthiest-ever muesli* (p.22) | 429 |
| | 1 chopped apple (skin included) | 60 |
| | 150 ml/5 fl oz unsweetened almond milk | 20 |
| Mid-morning snack | 35 g/1¼ oz reduced-fat Cheddar cheese | 110 |
| | 2 thin, round seeded oatcakes | 88 |
| Lunch | *Spicy chickpea and red pepper soup* (p.53) | 366 |
| | 2 *Beetroot brownie bites* (p.148) | 74 |
| | 1 tbsp full-fat Greek-style yogurt | 17 |
| Dinner | *Salmon ramen* (p.101) | 397 |
| | 60 g/2¼ oz (dry weight) brown basmati rice, cooked | 212 |
| Snack | 10 almonds and 4 walnut halves | 100 |

| **Day four** | **Total** (including milk allowance) | **1,898** |
|---|---|---|
| Breakfast | *Almond butter and raspberry smoothie* (p.26) | 338 |
| | 2 Brazil nuts | 66 |
| Mid-morning snack | *Cheese and herb scone* (p.138) | 213 |
| Lunch | *Pulled pork wrap* (p.59) | 467 |
| | 5 cherries | 25 |
| Dinner | *Tuna and broccoli pasta bake* (p.102) | 533 |
| | Large mixed leaf salad with 1 tbsp vinaigrette dressing | 60 |
| Dessert | 80 g/2¾ oz raspberries | 42 |
| Snack | 2 tsp *Home-made cashew nut butter* (p.128) | 76 |
| | 1 wholegrain, seeded rice cake | 28 |
| **Day five** | **Total** (including milk allowance) | **1,973** |
| Breakfast | *Carrot cake muffin* (p.33) | 318 |
| | 100 g/3½ oz blackberries | 43 |
| Mid-morning snack | *Cannellini bean dip with crudités* (p.124) | 184 |
| Lunch | *Beef rib-eye steak salad with rocket and Parmesan* (p.71) | 413 |
| | 30 g/1 oz almonds and 2 ready-to-eat dried apricots | 193 |
| Dinner | *Chicken and prawn jambalaya* (p.94) | 548 |
| Dessert | *Summer pudding* (p.153) | 224 |
| **Day six** | **Total** (including milk allowance) | **1,946** |
| Breakfast | *Potato pancakes with smoked salmon* (p.44) | 353 |
| | 1 orange | 60 |
| Mid-morning snack | 1 heaped tbsp *Home-made cashew nut butter* (p.128) | 153 |
| | 1 dark rye crispbread | 34 |
| Lunch | Avocado, tomato and mozzarella salad: ½ small (125 g/4½ oz) sliced avocado and 1 sliced tomato topped with 75 g/2¾ oz torn buffalo mozzarella, drizzled with balsamic vinegar and seasoned with salt and pepper | 435 |
| | 2 dark rye crispbreads | 68 |
| Dinner | *Winter root vegetable tagine* (p.108) | 458 |
| | 25 g/1 oz walnuts | 164 |
| Dessert | 80 g/2¾ oz raspberries | 39 |
| | 20 g/¾ oz melted or grated dark chocolate (70 per cent cocoa solids) | 120 |
| **Day seven** | **Total** (including milk allowance) | **1,928** |
| Breakfast | 1½ heaped tbsp *Home-made cashew nut butter* (p.128) | 230 |
| | 1 slice *Pumpernickel Bread* (p.137) | 135 |
| | ½ pink or red grapefruit | 42 |
| Mid-morning snack | *Cheese and herb scone* (p.138) | 213 |
| Lunch | *Smoked mackerel, beetroot and new potato salad* (p.72) | 435 |
| | 2 dark rye crispbreads | 68 |
| Dinner | *Chilli con carne* (p.80) | 622 |
| Dessert | 1 very small banana and 5 blueberries | 76 |
| | 100 g/3½ oz fat-free Greek-style yogurt | 57 |

## Plan 2: **Weight loss**

* **Calorie goal:** approximately 1,500 calories a day (based on average adult woman). Men should aim for approximately 2,000 calories a day and therefore increase portion sizes throughout by 33 per cent.

* **Consume freely:** leafy green vegetables and salad vegetables (such as lettuce, cucumber, radish and celery), fresh herbs and spices, lemon juice and vinegar.

* **To drink:** water and/or tea/coffee (with milk from allowance). Avoid alcohol.

* **Milk allowance:** 100 ml/3½ fl oz semi-skimmed milk (50 calories) for use in tea and coffee, or as you like. (Daily totals all include milk allowance.)

| | Recipe/Food | Calories |
|---|---|---|
| **Day one** | **Total (including milk allowance)** | **1,535** |
| Breakfast | *Spinach scramble with toasted rye bread* (p.40) | 247 |
| | ½ pink grapefruit | 42 |
| Mid-morning snack | *Mixed vegetable crisps* (p.127) | 128 |
| Lunch | *Mixed seafood chowder* (p.54) | 362 |
| | 1 small apple | 53 |
| Dinner | *Chinese marinated flank steak with noodles* (p.84) | 533 |
| Dessert | *Fluffy lemon whip* (p.156) | 120 |
| **Day two** | **Total (including milk allowance)** | **1,430** |
| Breakfast | Porridge: simmer 50 g/1¾ oz rolled oats with 275 ml/ 9 fl oz water until thick and soft. Stir in ½ tbsp milled linseeds and top with 50 ml/1¾ fl oz semi-skimmed milk | 229 |
| | 50 g/1¾ oz raspberries | 26 |
| Mid-morning snack | 1 large hard-boiled egg, 1 dark rye crispbread and 4 cherry tomatoes | 154 |
| Lunch | *Split pea and ham soup* (p.50) | 315 |
| | 25 g/1 oz slice wholegrain bread | 70 |
| Dinner | *Monkfish, mushroom and red pepper skewer* (p.99) | 429 |
| | Large mixed leaf and cucumber salad with 2 tsp balsamic vinegar | 9 |
| Dessert | 2 *Beetroot brownie bites* (p.148) | 74 |
| **Day three** | **Total (including milk allowance)** | **1,419** |
| Breakfast | *Nutty yogurt and melon sundae* (p.24) | 172 |
| | 1 slice *Pumpernickel bread*, toasted (p.137) | 135 |
| | 2 tsp extra-light spread | 10 |
| Mid-morning snack | *Oat, blueberry and nut cookie* (p.142) | 145 |
| Lunch | *Avocado, artichoke and almond salad* (p.67) | 364 |
| Dinner | *Chicken chow mein* (p.93) | 469 |
| Dessert | 1 *Beetroot brownie bite* (p.148) | 74 |

| **Day four** | **Total** (including milk allowance) | **1,446** |
|---|---|---|
| Breakfast | *Rustic blueberry, lemon and seed scone* (p.30) | 199 |
| | 1 small apple | 53 |
| Mid-morning snack | 25 g/1 oz *Fruit, nut and seed trail mix* (p.130) | 132 |
| Lunch | *Mini pizza muffin* (p.56) | 367 |
| | Large mixed leaf salad with 2 tsp vinaigrette dressing | 40 |
| Dinner | *Fish and chips* (p.96) | 412 |
| Dessert | *Vanilla custard cup with raspberry coulis* (p.154) | 151 |
| | 80 g/2¾ oz raspberries | 42 |
| **Day five** | **Total** (including milk allowance) | **1,489** |
| Breakfast | *Poached egg in tomato sauce* (p.38) | 312 |
| Mid-morning snack | 1 dark rye crispbread | 34 |
| | 2 tsp *Home-made cashew nut butter* (p.128) | 76 |
| Lunch | *Chicken and sweetcorn burrito* (p.60) | 361 |
| | 6 almonds | 34 |
| Dinner | *Butternut squash and spinach curry* (p.106) | 486 |
| | 1 tsp mango chutney | 16 |
| Dessert | 20 g/¾ oz dark chocolate (70 per cent cocoa solids) | 120 |
| **Day six** | **Total** (including milk allowance) | **1,453** |
| Breakfast | *Pancakes with creamy citrus filling* (p.29) | 316 |
| Mid-morning snack | 15 g/½ oz reduced-fat Cheddar cheese | 47 |
| | 1 thin, round seeded oatcake | 44 |
| Lunch | *Lentil and tuna salad* (p.75) | 225 |
| | 1 slice *Pumpernickel bread* (p.137) | 135 |
| | 1 plum | 30 |
| Dinner | 150 g/5½ oz hot-smoked salmon fillet | 312 |
| | 150 g/5½ oz new potatoes, steamed with skins on and cooled | 104 |
| | 80 g/2¾ oz each green beans and broccoli, steamed | 50 |
| | Juice of ¼ lemon | 0 |
| | 5 g/⅛ oz butter | 36 |
| Dessert | 60 g/2¼ oz ricotta cheese with 2 tsp stevia granules | 82 |
| | 50 g/1¾ oz blackberries | 22 |
| **Day seven** | **Total** (including milk allowance) | **1,454** |
| Breakfast | *Turkey sausage patties with mushrooms and tomatoes* (p.43) | 239 |
| | 25 g/1 oz slice wholegrain bread | 70 |
| Mid-morning snack | 10 almonds and 4 walnut halves | 98 |
| Lunch | *Crustless courgette and broad bean quiche* (p.64) | 412 |
| Dinner | *Lentil burger* (p.105) | 363 |
| | *Red cabbage, orange and walnut coleslaw* (p.120) | 148 |
| Dessert | 100 g/3½ oz fat-free Greek-style yogurt | 57 |
| | 30 g/1 oz blueberries | 17 |

# Breakfasts

1
2
2

# Coconut and blackberry porridge

Porridge is an ideal breakfast for controlling blood sugars, and the coconut and berries make it even more healthy and delicious.

*Calories 322 // Carbohydrates 38.7 g // Sugars 9.9 g // Protein 10.6 g // Fibre 7.3 g // Fat 15.2 g // Saturated fat 4.1 g // Salt 1.3 g*

250 ml/9 fl oz coconut water
200 ml/7 fl oz water
200 ml/7 fl oz skimmed milk
150 g/5½ oz porridge oats
½ tsp ground mixed spice
1 tsp salt
2 tsp stevia granules
80 g/2¾ oz low-fat natural yogurt

**To serve**
100 g/3½ oz blackberries
60 g/2¼ oz hazelnuts, chopped
20 g/¾ oz desiccated coconut

1. Place the coconut water, water and milk in a saucepan and stir well to combine.

2. Stir in the oats, mixed spice, salt, stevia granules and yogurt and bring to a simmer. Reduce the heat and gently simmer, stirring frequently, for 10 minutes, or until the porridge is thick and creamy and the oats are tender.

3. Transfer to serving dishes. Top with the blackberries and sprinkle over the chopped hazelnuts and desiccated coconut. Serve immediately.

*Serves: 4 // Preparation time: 10 minutes // Cooking time: 15 minutes*

Stevia is a natural leaf-based sweetener and a healthy alternative to sugar or artificial sweeteners. You can find it in granular or liquid form and it is virtually calorie-free with no effect on blood sugars.

*Tip //*

# Healthiest-ever muesli

Most shop-bought mueslis contain very high levels of dried fruits and are thus high in sugars. This version contains a much healthier level of sugar.

*Calories 429 // Carbohydrates 53.5 g // Sugars 5.6 g // Protein 14.0 g // Fibre 10.9 g // Fat 20.2 g // Saturated fat 3.0 g // Salt Trace*

150 g/5½ oz oat flakes
100 g/3½ oz rye flakes
40 g/1½ oz walnuts
40 g/1½ oz Brazil nuts
10 g/¼ oz sunflower seeds
10 g/¼ oz pumpkin seeds
15 g/½ oz raisins
15 g/½ oz ready-to-eat dried apricots, chopped
2 tbsp milled flaxseed

*Tip //*

Milled flaxseed is readily available in supermarkets. The milling process means the nutrients in the ground seeds are much better absorbed than those in whole seeds, which tend to pass through the digestive system whole.

1. In a mixing bowl, thoroughly combine the oat flakes and rye flakes.

2. Chop the walnuts and Brazil nuts and add to the flakes with the sunflower seeds, pumpkin seeds and raisins.

3. Mix the dried apricots with the milled flaxseed – the seed meal will coat the apricots and prevent them from sticking together. Stir into the muesli.

4. Store in an airtight container if not using immediately. You can easily double or treble the quantity and store in the refrigerator for 1 week.

*Serves: 4 // Preparation time: 10 minutes // Cooking time: None*

# Nutty yogurt and melon sundaes

Colourful and tempting, this refreshing breakfast is a perfect start to the day when you feel like something light.

*Calories 172 // Carbohydrates 14.2 g // Sugars 10.0 g // Protein 12.0 g // Fibre 2.1 g // Fat 8.3 g // Saturated fat 1.3 g // Salt 0.2 g*

- 200 g/7 oz low-fat bio yogurt
- 200 g/7 oz low-fat soft cheese or quark
- 1 tsp stevia granules
- 30 g/1 oz pistachio nuts, roughly chopped
- 30 g/1 oz toasted flaked almonds
- 200 g/7 oz watermelon chunks
- 30 g/1 oz pomegranate seeds

*Tip //*

Similar in texture to mascarpone but with no fat, no added sugar and a great protein content, quark is a good addition to your diet. Just 100 g/ 3½ oz contains nearly your whole daily requirement of calcium.

1. In a mixing bowl, thoroughly combine the yogurt, soft cheese and stevia granules.

2. Stir in half the pistachio nuts and flaked almonds.

3. Divide the watermelon chunks between four serving glasses and spoon a quarter of the yogurt mixture over the top of each.

4. Sprinkle with the remaining nuts, followed by the pomegranate seeds, and serve the sundaes immediately.

*Serves: 4 // Preparation time: 10 minutes // Cooking time: None*

1
2
3

# Almond butter and raspberry smoothies

If you don't usually eat breakfast, try this smoothie. It is a really quick and tasty breakfast that is packed with nutrients.

*Calories 338 // Carbohydrates 28.4 g // Sugars 11.6 g // Protein 6.7 g // Fibre 10.7 g // Fat 14.1 g // Saturated fat 1.0 g // Salt 0.2 g*

1 banana
200 g/7 oz raspberries
400 ml/14 fl oz unsweetened almond milk
40 g/1½ oz almond butter
4 tsp stevia granules
2 tsp vanilla extract
ice cubes

*Tip //*

Bananas are a rich source of potassium and resistant starch, both of which have benefits for diabetics. Potassium appears to help to regulate the production of insulin while resistant starch increases insulin sensitivity.

1. Peel the banana and place in a blender with the raspberries.

2. Add the almond milk, almond butter, stevia granules and vanilla extract. Top up with ice cubes.

3. Blend until smooth. Drink immediately or store in the refrigerator overnight.

*Serves: 2 // Preparation time: 10 minutes // Cooking time: None*

1

2

3

1

2

4

# Pancakes with creamy citrus filling

This breakfast has a great balance of protein, carbohydrates and fat. The rye and spelt flours give the pancakes a nutty, slightly sweet taste.

*Calories 316 // Carbohydrates 35.8 g // Sugars 9.1 g // Protein 19.7 g // Fibre 3.4 g // Fat 10.7 g // Saturated fat 4.3 g // Salt 1.6 g*

250 g/9 oz ricotta cheese
200 g/7 oz fat-free Greek-style yogurt
1 tbsp grated orange rind
2 tbsp orange juice
1–2 tsp stevia granules, or to taste
40 g/1½ oz rye flour
40 g/1½ oz spelt flour or wholemeal flour
40 g/1½ oz plain flour
1 tsp salt
2 small eggs
1 tbsp groundnut oil
150 ml/5 fl oz skimmed milk
100 ml/3½ fl oz water
cooking spray, for oiling
1 orange, peeled, segmented and chopped
2 tsp icing sugar, for dusting

1. In a bowl, combine the ricotta, yogurt, orange rind, orange juice and stevia granules. Set aside in the refrigerator until ready to serve.

2. In a mixing bowl, stir together the rye flour, spelt flour, plain flour and salt, then whisk in the eggs, oil, milk and water until completely smooth.

3. Heat a small, non-stick frying pan over a medium–high heat and coat with cooking spray.

4. When the pan is hot, pour in a quarter of the batter and swirl it around to coat the pan. Cook for 1 minute, or until the underside is golden, then flip the pancake over with a spatula and cook for 1 minute on the other side. Transfer the cooked pancake to a warmed plate while you cook the remaining batter.

5. Repeat to make three more pancakes, spraying the pan between each addition. (You could make eight mini pancakes, if you prefer.)

6. Place the pancakes on serving plates, then fill with the ricotta mixture and a little of the chopped orange and fold over. Decorate with the remaining chopped orange and dust with the icing sugar.

*Serves: 4 // Preparation time: 20 minutes // Cooking time: 10 minutes*

Spelt is an ancient cousin of modern wheat that is enjoying a revival today and is widely available both as flour and whole grains. As it contains more fat and protein than wheat it has a useful lower GI rating.

*Tip //*

# Rustic blueberry, lemon and seed scones

These unique, rustic-looking scones are made using a tasty, nutrient-rich seeded flour, as well as flaxseeds and blueberries.

*Calories 199 // Carbohydrates 25.9 g // Sugars 3.8 g // Protein 6.0 g // Fibre 2.9 g // Fat 7.3 g // Saturated fat 1.4 g // Salt 1.2 g*

cooking spray, for oiling
275 g/9¾ oz wholemeal seeded flour, plus extra for dusting
100 g/3½ oz oatmeal
15 g/½ oz milled flaxseed
2 tsp baking powder
½ tsp bicarbonate of soda
1 tsp salt
3 heaped tbsp stevia granules
125 g/4½ oz small blueberries
grated rind of 1 lemon
275 ml/9 fl oz low-fat natural yogurt
2 tbsp groundnut oil
juice of ½ lemon
100 ml/3½ fl oz skimmed milk
120 g/4¼ oz reduced-fat sunflower spread, to serve

1. Preheat the oven to 200°C/400°F/Gas Mark 6. Spray a baking tray with cooking spray.

2. Put the flour, oatmeal, milled flaxseed, baking powder, bicarbonate of soda, salt and stevia granules into a large mixing bowl and thoroughly combine with a fork. Stir in the blueberries and lemon rind.

3. Put the yogurt, oil, lemon juice and milk into a jug and whisk together.

4. Pour the yogurt mixture into the flour mixture and stir until you have a rough dough.

5. Flour your hands and divide the mixture into 12 rough balls and place on the prepared baking tray. Bake in the preheated oven for 15 minutes, or until the scones are golden and firm.

6. Leave to cool for 10 minutes, then spread each scone with 10 g/¼ oz sunflower spread and eat warm or cold. The scones can be stored in an airtight container for 1–2 days, or can be frozen in a strong polythene bag for up to 1 month.

*Makes: 12 // Preparation time: 20–25 minutes // Cooking time: 15 minutes, plus cooling*

Natural yogurt is a great ingredient to use in baking for diabetics because it has a low GI rating of just 14. Other ingredients that bring down the glycaemic load of these scones are the seeds, oats, blueberries and oil.

*Tip //*

1
2
5

1
3
5

# Carrot cake muffins

These delicious carrot, raisin and walnut muffins are surprisingly low in sugar and fat, and are packed with fibre and vitamin A-rich carrots.

*Calories 318 // Carbohydrates 47.0 g // Sugars 9.0 g // Protein 9.0 g // Fibre 7.9 g // Fat 12.5 g // Saturated fat 4.2 g // Salt 1.0 g*

450 g/1 lb plain wholemeal flour
1 tsp bicarbonate of soda
1 tsp baking powder
½ tsp salt
1 tsp ground cinnamon
¼ tsp ground ginger
2 tbsp rapeseed oil
1 egg
2 egg whites
3 tbsp stevia granules
2 tsp vanilla extract
120 g/4¼ oz unsweetened apple sauce
80 ml/2¾ fl oz unsweetened almond milk
450 g/1 lb carrots
80 g/2¾ oz raisins
60 g/2¼ oz walnuts, chopped
60 g/2¼ oz desiccated coconut

1. Preheat the oven to 180°C/350°F/Gas Mark 4. Line ten holes in a 12-hole muffin tin with paper cases.

2. Sift together the flour, bicarbonate of soda, baking powder, salt, cinnamon and ginger into a bowl, adding any bran left in the sieve.

3. Beat together the oil, egg, egg whites, stevia granules and vanilla extract in a bowl until creamy, then stir in the apple sauce and almond milk.

4. Peel and grate the carrots, then add to the liquid ingredients with the raisins, walnuts and half the desiccated coconut. Add the flour mixture, stirring until just combined.

5. Divide the mixture between the paper cases. Bake in the preheated oven for 25 minutes, or until a skewer inserted into the centre of a muffin comes out clean.

6. Leave to cool in the tin until cool enough to handle, then transfer to a wire rack to cool completely. Decorate with the remaining desiccated coconut or wrap in polythene bags and freeze for up to 1 month.

*Makes: 10 // Preparation time: 20–25 minutes // Cooking time: 25 minutes, plus cooling*

Almond milk is becoming very popular across the world as an alternative to cow's milk. The unsweetened version contains just 0.1 per cent sugar, compared to 5 per cent sugar in dairy milk.

*Tip //*

# Building activity into your day

If you are diabetic, or want to help prevent yourself from developing diabetes, the argument for getting moving is strong. Many studies across the world have found that activity is critical for optimum health in those with insulin resistance, pre-diabetes, Type 2 diabetes, gestational diabetes and diabetes-related health complications, such as poor bone health. Even moderate exercise improves insulin action and can assist with the management of blood glucose levels, lipids, blood pressure and cardiovascular risk, as well as improving stress levels, sleep and mood.

Do ask your health practitioner for help in deciding what is best for you, and then try our tips for building more activity into your everyday life.

* If you're currently mostly sedentary, you need to start gently – even simply getting up and standing more often (for example, when talking on the phone or waiting for the kettle to boil) is a good start.

* Small, manageable chunks of activity are usually the way to go after that. Everyday things like walking up the stairs or inclines, dancing in the sitting room to the radio, or gardening are all great.

* Think about one extra activity you could try that would fit in well with your current lifestyle. For example, walking with added pleasure – with binoculars to spot birds, with a camera, or with a friend. If you sleep poorly, a 15-minute walk after supper in the spring and summer months is ideal.

* There's no need to worry about going to a gym, which can often be expensive and a long way to travel. You can buy inexpensive resistance bands or a basic rowing machine and do some exercise at home – even while you watch TV!

* Once or twice a day, try to get your heart rate up – this means you'll feel warm, perhaps break into a light sweat and know your lungs are working harder. This could happen during everyday tasks, such as housework, car cleaning or gardening. Try to put effort into the chores and think about swapping electrical appliances for 'elbow grease' – for example, by using a broom instead of a vacuum cleaner or car-washing by hand rather than with a hose.

* When you need to go out to get a newspaper or milk or so on, only use the car if you really need to. Think about walking or even cycling to the shops. Carrying shopping home is a great way to get fitter, burn calories and improve muscle strength.

* If you commute, consider getting off the bus or train a stop early and walking the rest of the way, or park the car further away from your workplace. During the working day, stand up whenever you can, walk over to your colleagues' desks to speak to them rather than telephoning or emailing, and use the stairs instead of the escalator or lift. Don't work through your lunch break at your desk either – get out for some fresh air.

# Eggs Benedict with asparagus and Parma ham

If you are a fan of bacon and eggs, try this – it is rich in protein and fat, which will keep hunger pangs at bay until lunchtime.

*Calories 342 // Carbohydrates 15.0 g // Sugars 3.3 g // Protein 20.6 g // Fibre 2.8 g // Fat 25.0 g // Saturated fat 6.0 g // Salt 2.4 g*

*Tip //*

When you buy eggs, remember that eggs from hens that are allowed to forage and roam freely have a considerably higher Omega-3 fat content than most eggs from caged hens.

8 asparagus spears
4 large eggs
cooking spray, for oiling
8 slices Parma ham
100 g/3½ oz light mayonnaise
1 tbsp melted butter
1 heaped tsp Dijon mustard
1 tbsp lemon juice
2 wholemeal English muffins
pepper
pinch of cayenne pepper, to garnish

1. Steam the asparagus spears for 5 minutes, or until just tender. Drain and set aside.

2. Meanwhile, poach the eggs in a saucepan of barely simmering water until the whites are set and the yolks are still runny. Transfer to kitchen paper to drain, set aside and keep warm.

3. Spray a frying pan with cooking spray to coat, then add the Parma ham and fry for 1 minute, or until golden and slightly crisp.

4. Beat together the mayonnaise, melted butter, mustard, lemon juice and pepper to taste in a bowl.

5. Meanwhile, preheat the grill to medium. Split and lightly toast the muffins.

6. Spread each toasted muffin half with a little of the mayonnaise sauce and top with two slices of the Parma ham, two asparagus spears and a poached egg. Pour over the remaining sauce and garnish with a sprinkling of cayenne pepper. Serve immediately.

*Serves: 4 // Preparation time: 10–15 minutes // Cooking time: 15 mins*

1
2
4

# Poached eggs in tomato sauce

Simple and unbelievably delicious, this rustic dish of eggs lightly poached in bubbling tomato sauce is perfect for breakfast or brunch.

*Calories 312 // Carbohydrates 31.0 g // Sugars 6.4 g // Protein 14.3 g // Fibre 4.5 g // Fat 13.0 g // Saturated fat 3.5 g // Salt 2.3 g*

1 tbsp olive oil
1 small onion, diced
2 garlic cloves, finely chopped
½ tsp salt
½ tsp pepper
¼ tsp chilli flakes
4 tbsp red wine
400 g/14 oz canned chopped tomatoes
2 tsp finely chopped fresh oregano, thyme, basil, sage or other herb
4 eggs
4 slices wholemeal rustic bread, about 45 g/1½ oz each
2 tbsp finely chopped Kalamata olives
4 tbsp freshly grated Parmesan cheese

1. Heat the oil in a large frying pan over a medium–high heat. Add the onion and garlic and cook, stirring occasionally, for about 5 minutes, or until soft. Add the salt, pepper, chilli flakes and wine and cook for a further few minutes until the liquid has mostly evaporated.

2. Add the tomatoes and their juice, bring to the boil, then reduce the heat to medium–low and simmer for about 15–20 minutes, or until the sauce thickens. Stir in the herbs.

3. Make four wells in the sauce and carefully crack the eggs into them. Cover and simmer for about 7–9 minutes, or until the whites are set but the yolks are still runny.

4. Meanwhile, preheat the grill to medium and lightly toast the bread.

5. Put the slices of toast on four plates. Carefully scoop the eggs out of the sauce and place one on each slice of toast. Place spoonfuls of the sauce around the egg and top with a sprinkling of chopped olives and grated Parmesan cheese. Serve immediately.

*Serves: 4 // Preparation time: 10–15 minutes // Cooking time: 35–40 minutes*

Tomatoes are rich in potassium, which helps to control high blood pressure, and contain a great range of carotenes as well as vitamins C and E. Research shows that cooking tomatoes in a little oil allows our bodies to absorb these health-giving nutrients more easily.

*Tip //*

# Spinach scramble with toasted rye bread

The addition of spinach and rye bread in this recipe turns scrambled eggs into something extra-healthy, not to mention extra-yummy!

*Calories 247 // Carbohydrates 18.0 g // Sugars 2.1 g // Protein 15.3 g // Fibre 2.8 g // Fat 12.4 g // Saturated fat 4.8 g // Salt 2.2 g*

*Tip //*

Delicious wholegrain rye bread is believed to improve blood sugar control and regulate appetite. Spinach is rich in vitamin K for bone health, and also in vitamin C, which helps the good amounts of iron in both the eggs and spinach to be absorbed.

175 g/6 oz young spinach leaves, roughly shredded
8 eggs
3 tbsp skimmed milk
15 g/½ oz butter
4 slices rye bread, about 30 g/1 oz each
salt and pepper
freshly grated nutmeg, to serve

1. Heat a large frying pan over a high heat and add the spinach. Stir for 1–2 minutes, or until the leaves are wilted. Remove from the heat, tip into a sieve and squeeze out as much of the excess moisture as possible. Set aside and keep warm.

2. Break the eggs into a bowl, add the milk and season to taste with salt and pepper. Beat lightly with a fork until evenly mixed.

3. Melt the butter in the pan over a medium heat. Add the eggs and stir until just beginning to set. Add the spinach and stir until lightly set.

4. Meanwhile, preheat the grill to medium and lightly toast the rye bread.

5. Spoon the spinach scramble over the toast, sprinkle with grated nutmeg and serve immediately.

*Serves: 4 // Preparation time: 10 minutes // Cooking time: 8–10 minutes*

1

2

3

1
2
3

# Turkey sausage patties with mushrooms and tomatoes

These high-protein patties make a wonderful change from regular sausages at breakfast time – they are also great for dinner served with new potatoes.

*Calories 239 // Carbohydrates 13.8 g // Sugars 5.0 g // Protein 26.0 g // Fibre 2.7 g // Fat 9.4 g // Saturated fat 2.2 g // Salt 1.7 g*

400 g/14 oz fresh turkey mince
1 tsp salt
1 tsp pepper
1 tsp dried thyme
1 tsp dried sage
½ tsp ground allspice
3 garlic cloves, crushed
4 tbsp oatmeal
1 small egg, beaten
3 tsp light olive oil
400 g/14 oz chestnut mushrooms, sliced
4 tomatoes, cut into wedges

1. Thoroughly combine the turkey with the salt, pepper, thyme, sage, allspice, garlic, oatmeal and egg in a bowl. (The mixture can be stored, covered, in the refrigerator for up to 12 hours.)

2. Shape the mixture into eight small patties. Heat 2 teaspoons of the oil in a non-stick frying pan, add the patties and fry over a medium heat for about 4 minutes on each side, or until golden and cooked all the way through with no pink inside. Transfer to a plate and keep warm.

3. Add the mushrooms to the pan and stir for 1 minute, until soft. Pour in the remaining oil, then add the tomatoes and cook, without stirring, for a further 1–2 minutes to warm through. Serve the patties with the mushrooms and tomatoes.

*Serves: 4 // Preparation time: 15–20 minutes // Cooking time: 15 minutes*

If you have a food processor or electric chopper you can buy turkey leg meat and mince it yourself – the dark leg meat of the turkey contains more B vitamins, selenium, iron and zinc than the light breast meat.

*Tip //*

# Potato pancakes with smoked salmon

These crispy potato pancakes topped with dollops of soured cream and slices of smoked salmon are just the thing for a lazy brunch.

*Calories 353 // Carbohydrates 38.0 g // Sugars 4.4 g // Protein 18.3 g // Fibre 4.8 g // Fat 14.3 g // Saturated fat 3.6 g // Salt 2.5 g*

600 g/1 lb 5 oz potatoes, coarsely grated
1 large onion, grated
2 eggs, lightly beaten
55 g/2 oz stale wholemeal breadcrumbs
1 tsp salt
2 tbsp sunflower oil
100 g/3½ oz reduced-fat soured cream
200 g/7 oz thinly sliced smoked salmon
pepper
snipped fresh chives, to garnish

1. Preheat the oven to 110°C/225°F/Gas Mark ¼ (or its lowest setting). Line a heatproof plate with kitchen paper.

2. Working in small batches, put the grated potatoes on a tea towel, fold over the tea towel and squeeze to extract as much water as possible.

3. Put the potatoes in a large bowl and add the onion, eggs, breadcrumbs, the salt, and pepper to taste. Mix together well.

4. Heat a large, heavy-based frying pan over a medium–high heat. Add half the oil and heat until hot. Drop 2 tablespoons of the mixture into the pan and flatten slightly. Add as many more pancakes as will fit without overcrowding the pan. Fry for 2 minutes, or until crisp and golden underneath. Flip or turn with a palette knife and continue frying for a further 1–2 minutes, until crisp and golden.

5. Repeat using the remaining mixture and oil. Meanwhile, transfer the cooked pancakes to the prepared plate and keep warm in the oven.

6. Serve the pancakes hot, topped with the soured cream and smoked salmon. Garnish with chives.

*Serves: 4 // Preparation time: 15–20 minutes // Cooking time: 8–10 minutes*

Coarsely grating potatoes, as in this recipe, rather than mashing them, helps slow down the rate at which they are absorbed into the digestive system and thus helps minimise the risk of a spike in blood sugars.

*Tip //*

# Lunches

# Chicken noodle soup

Chicken noodle soup is the perfect comfort food. It is low in fat and saturates and a good source of protein and fibre.

*Calories 336 // Carbohydrates 35.9 g // Sugars 5.0 g // Protein 30.6 g // Fibre 5.3 g // Fat 7.7 g // Saturated fat 1.7 g // Salt 1.7 g*

1. Heat the oil in a saucepan over a medium heat. Add the onion, celery and carrot and cook, stirring occasionally, for 8 minutes, until soft but not brown.

2. Add the garlic and cook for 1 minute. Add the chicken to the pan with the beans, stock and pepper to taste. Bring to the boil, then reduce the heat and simmer for 5 minutes.

3. Add the noodles to the pan, return to a simmer and cook for 5 minutes, or until the noodles are just tender. Garnish the soup with coriander leaves and serve immediately.

*Serves: 4 // Preparation time: 15 minutes // Cooking time: 25 minutes*

1 tbsp groundnut oil
1 onion, finely chopped
2 celery sticks, finely chopped
1 large carrot, finely chopped
2 garlic cloves, crushed
400 g/14 oz skinless, boneless chicken breasts, cut into bite-sized pieces
150 g/5½ oz fine French beans, cut into 3-cm/1¼-inch pieces
1.2 litres/2 pints reduced-salt chicken stock
150 g/5½ oz dried wholemeal egg noodles
pepper
small bunch of fresh coriander leaves, to garnish

Groundnut – or peanut – oil is an excellent oil to use for frying as it contains a great balance of healthy monounsaturated and polyunsaturated fats. It also has a high smoke point, unlike, for example, virgin olive oil.

*Tip //*

1
2
3

# Split pea and ham soup

Many soups are quite low in protein, but not this one – it is packed with protein-rich split peas. It needs to be cooked slowly to develop the flavours.

*Calories 315 // Carbohydrates 47.1 g // Sugars 8.1 g // Protein 24.1 g // Fibre 18.7 g // Fat 4.4 g // Saturated fat 1.1 g // Salt 1.9 g*

500 g/1 lb 2 oz split green peas
1 tbsp olive oil
1 large onion, finely chopped
1 large carrot, finely chopped
1 celery stick, finely chopped
1 litre/1¾ pints reduced-salt vegetable stock
1 litre/1¾ pints water
225 g/8 oz lean smoked ham, finely diced
¼ tsp dried thyme
¼ tsp dried marjoram
1 bay leaf
salt and pepper

1. Rinse the peas under cold running water. Put them in a saucepan and cover with water. Bring to the boil and boil for 3 minutes, skimming off any foam from the surface, if necessary. Drain the peas.

2. Heat the oil in a large saucepan over a medium heat. Add the onion and cook for 3–4 minutes, stirring occasionally, until just softened. Add the carrot and celery and continue cooking for 2 minutes.

3. Add the peas, pour over the stock and water and stir to combine.

4. Bring just to the boil and stir the ham into the soup. Add the thyme, marjoram and bay leaf. Reduce the heat, cover and cook gently for 1–1½ hours, until the ingredients are very soft. Remove the bay leaf.

5. Taste and adjust the seasoning. Ladle into warmed soup bowls and serve.

*Serves: 8 // Preparation time: 15 minutes // Cooking time: 1¼ hours–1¾ hours*

Split peas are easily digested pulses that are high in resistant starch to maintain stable blood sugar levels. They are a great source of heart-friendly soluble fibre too, which helps to lower blood LDL (bad) cholesterol.

*Tip //*

1

2

4

# Spicy chickpea and red pepper soup

Chickpeas have been shown to help regulate blood sugars and improve satiety after a meal, making them a useful ingredient in this tasty soup.

*Calories 366 // Carbohydrates 44.8 g // Sugars 10.0 g // Protein 13.3 g // Fibre 10.4 g // Fat 14.6 g // Saturated fat 2.7 g // Salt 0.6 g*

2½ tbsp olive oil
6 spring onions, chopped
1 large fresh red jalapeño chilli, deseeded and finely sliced
4 garlic cloves, finely chopped
2 tsp ground cumin
1 tsp chilli powder
3 fresh ripe tomatoes, peeled and roughly chopped
400 g/14 oz ready-roasted red peppers in water, drained and thinly sliced
1 tbsp red pepper pesto
1 litre/1¾ pints reduced-salt vegetable stock
400 g/14 oz canned chickpeas, drained and rinsed
1 tsp stevia granules
2 tsp red wine vinegar
100 g/3½ oz baby spinach leaves
pepper
4 slices oat bread, about 45 g/1½ oz each, to serve

1. Heat the oil in a large saucepan over a medium heat. Add the spring onions and cook for 2–3 minutes, stirring occasionally, until soft.

2. Add the chilli, garlic, cumin and chilli powder and cook for 1 minute, stirring.

3. Stir in the tomatoes, red peppers, pesto and stock and bring to a simmer. Cook for 10 minutes, then add the chickpeas, stevia granules, vinegar and pepper to taste and cook for a further 5 minutes.

4. Stir in the spinach and cook for 1 minute, until the spinach wilts. Serve with the oat bread.

*Serves: 4 // Preparation time: 15 minutes // Cooking time: 25 minutes*

For a thicker soup, tip half of the soup into a blender at the end of step 3 (before adding the spinach) and blend. Return to the pan with the rest of the soup and stir well.

*Tip //*

# Mixed seafood chowder

Chowder is a classic American East Coast main-meal soup, often made with clams. This mixed seafood version is equally good.

*Calories 362 // Carbohydrates 22.7 g // Sugars 6.7 g // Protein 30.4 g // Fibre 2.3 g // Fat 15.5 g // Saturated fat 5.0 g // Salt 2.7 g*

1 tbsp vegetable oil
1 large onion, chopped
80 g/2¾ oz cubed pancetta
1 tbsp plain flour
600 ml/1 pint fish stock, made from 1 fish stock cube
225 g/8 oz small new potatoes, halved
pinch of saffron threads
pinch of cayenne pepper
300 ml/10 fl oz semi-skimmed milk
200 g/7 oz haddock or other white fish fillet, cubed
150 g/5½ oz salmon fillet, cubed
200 g/7 oz cooked shelled mussels
pepper

1. Heat the oil in a large saucepan over a medium heat, then add the onion and pancetta. Cook for 8–10 minutes, until the onion is soft and the pancetta is cooked. Stir in the flour and cook for a further 2 minutes.

2. Stir in the stock and bring to a gentle simmer. Add the potatoes, then cover and simmer for 10–12 minutes, until the potatoes are tender and cooked through.

3. Add the saffron, cayenne pepper and pepper to taste, then stir in the milk. Tip the fish into the pan and simmer gently for 4 minutes.

4. Add the mussels and cook for a further 2 minutes to warm through. Serve immediately.

*Serves: 4 // Preparation time: 10 minutes // Cooking time: 30–35 minutes*

Both the pancetta and fish stock are quite high in salt so you won't need to add any more salt to the chowder. If you don't have any saffron threads, you can use ½ teaspoon of sweet paprika instead.

*Tip //*

1

2

4

# Mini pizza muffins

It's great to think that you can have a hearty lunch containing bread, cheese and crispy ham, knowing its nutrient content is just fine.

*Calories 367 // Carbohydrates 38.6 g // Sugars 10.3 g // Protein 25.8 g // Fibre 7.1 g // Fat 11.7 g // Saturated fat 5.3 g // Salt 2.3 g*

*Tip //*

These muffins are high in fibre because there are plenty of veggies in each portion, and the wholemeal flour in the muffins adds more. Wholemeal muffins are readily available in supermarkets.

2 wholemeal English muffins
125 g/4½ oz ready-made tomato pasta sauce with mushrooms
1 tomato, sliced
80 g/2¾ oz chestnut mushrooms, sliced
1 ready-roasted green or yellow pepper in water, drained and sliced (100 g/3½ oz drained weight)
2 slices Parma ham, each torn in half
125 g/4½ oz reduced-fat mozzarella cheese, sliced
8 black olives, stoned and sliced

1. Preheat the oven to 180°C/350°F/Gas Mark 4. Split the muffins and arrange the halves, cut-side up, on a baking tray.

2. Spread a thin layer of tomato sauce on the muffin halves, then top with the sliced tomato and mushrooms.

3. Divide the green pepper between the muffin halves, then top with the Parma ham, mozzarella cheese and black olives.

4. Bake in the preheated oven for 15 minutes, or until the cheese is melted and the muffins are toasted. Serve immediately.

*Serves: 2 // Preparation time: 10 minutes // Cooking time: 15 minutes*

1
2
3

1

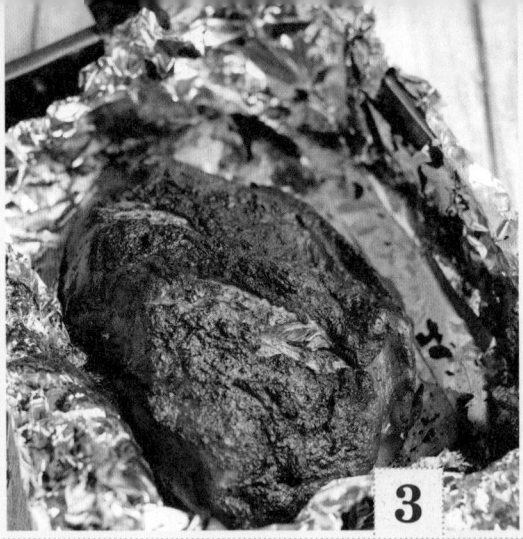
3

4

# Pulled pork wraps

Slow-cooked pulled pork is deservedly popular and these wraps won't disappoint. The leftover pork can be frozen for another time.

*Calories 467 // Carbohydrates 43.8 g // Sugars 10.1 g // Protein 24.3 g // Fibre 3.9 g // Fat 17.1 g // Saturated fat 1.2 g // Salt 2.3 g*

1 small pork shoulder joint, about 1 kg/2 lb 4 oz, skin removed
1 tsp salt
2 tsp sweet paprika
2 tsp soft light brown sugar
1 tsp Dijon mustard
100 ml/3½ fl oz reduced-salt chicken stock

**To serve**
8 crisp lettuce leaves
6 spring onions, chopped
¼ cucumber, chopped
20 g/¾ oz fresh coriander leaves
1 mild red chilli, sliced
3 tbsp chilli dipping sauce
juice of ½ lime
4 multigrain tortillas

1. Preheat the oven to 220°C/425°F/Gas Mark 7. Line a roasting tin with a sheet of aluminium foil large enough to cover the pork. Place the pork in the tin, rub ½ teaspoon of the salt and 1 teaspoon of the paprika into the skin and cook in the preheated oven (without covering) for 30 minutes.

2. Reduce the oven temperature to 150°C/300°F/Gas Mark 2. Rub the remaining salt and paprika into the pork with the sugar and mustard. Pour in the stock and loosely cover with the foil. Cook for a further 3 hours, or until the pork is soft and a piece comes away from the joint easily when pulled with a fork.

3. Increase the oven temperature to 220°C/425°F/Gas Mark 7 and cook the pork for a further 20 minutes, until crisp on the outside. Remove from the oven and leave to rest, covered, for 30 minutes.

4. Pull the pork into pieces with two forks. Pour any cooking juices over the pulled pork and stir to combine. Weigh out 400 g/14 oz of the pork and use this to make the wraps.

5. Divide the pork, lettuce, spring onions, cucumber, coriander, chilli, chilli sauce and lime juice between the wraps. Serve immediately.

*Serves: 4 // Preparation time: 20 minutes // Cooking time: 3 hours 50 minutes, plus resting*

You can use the leftover pulled pork cold to fill a wholemeal sandwich or pitta, along with plenty of salad.

*Tip //*

# Chicken and sweetcorn burritos

Burritos are fantastic fun to make and you can vary the ingredients – try black beans instead of pinto beans and use turkey instead of chicken.

*Calories 361 // Carbohydrates 39.2 g // Sugars 4.6 g // Protein 22.1 g // Fibre 6.2 g // Fat 12.6 g // Saturated fat 4.1 g // Salt 1.3 g*

*Tip //*

These tasty lunch snacks have an almost perfect nutritional profile – they are low in fat and saturates, and packed with protein, fibre and resistant starch to keep your blood sugars on an even keel.

1 tbsp olive oil
225 g/8 oz skinless, boneless chicken breasts, cut into strips
125 g/4½ oz sweetcorn kernels
100 g/3½ oz canned pinto beans, drained and rinsed
100 g/3½ oz ready-to-eat quinoa
2 tsp hot chilli sauce
juice of 1 lime
100 g/3½ oz light soft cheese with garlic and herbs
100 g/3½ oz white cabbage, thinly shredded
4 wholemeal tortillas
20 g/¾ oz fresh coriander leaves
pepper

1. Heat the oil in a non-stick frying pan over a high heat. Add the chicken to the pan and stir for 1–2 minutes, or until golden. Stir in the sweetcorn and beans and cook until the corn is slightly browned.

2. Add the quinoa, chilli sauce, lime juice, soft cheese, cabbage and pepper to taste. Cook, stirring, over a medium–high heat for a few minutes, until the cheese is melted.

3. Divide the mixture between the tortillas, sprinkle over the coriander and roll up. Serve immediately.

*Serves: 4 // Preparation time: 10 minutes // Cooking time: 8–10 minutes*

1
2
3

# Top ten superfoods for diabetes

### *1. Pulses*

Pulses, such as chickpeas, lentils and kidney beans, are high in soluble fibres, insoluble fibres and resistant starch; have a good carbohydrate to protein ratio; boast a low GI rating of around 30; and contain essential vitamins and minerals – making them an all-round superfood for diabetics. Research shows that regularly eating pulses can reduce the risk of heart disease, control blood sugar levels and lower blood pressure.

### *2. Oily fish*

Fish, such as salmon, mackerel and fresh tuna, are our best sources of healthy Omega-3 fats, which lower the risk of heart disease by improving the blood fats profile, slowing the growth rate of arterial plaques and lowering blood pressure. The fat is also anti-inflammatory, and oily fish has a great content of vitamin D, deficiency of which may be linked to Type 2 diabetes.

### *3. Nuts*

There is evidence that nuts can improve blood sugar control in Type 2 diabetics and can also reduce LDL (low density lipoproteins or 'bad') cholesterol and even help with weight loss. Nuts are very low on the Glycaemic Index and contain important nutrients including monounsaturated and polyunsaturated fats, magnesium and vitamin E.

### *4. Seeds*

Flaxseed, pine nuts, sunflower seeds and pumpkin seeds are particularly good sources of essential fats and monounsaturated fats. Flaxseed is high in the Omega-3 fat ALA (alpha linolenic acid), linked with protection from heart disease, stroke and inflammation. Diets supplemented with flaxseed result in lowered fasting blood glucose levels and reduced blood pressure, total cholesterol, and LDL cholesterol.

### *5. Oats*

Oats are full of soluble and insoluble fibre, which help to metabolize fats, keep the digestive track healthy and keep blood sugar stable by delaying the speed at which the stomach empties. Compared to other grains, oats have a higher proportion of soluble fibre, which can help to lower LDL cholesterol and decrease the risk of heart disease.

## *6. Berries*

Berries have among the lowest GI ratings of all fruit types and can help with blood sugar control. They are also high in plant compounds called anthocyanins – a large study published in the American Journal of Clinical Nutrition has found that people who regularly consume berries have up to 23 per cent lower risk of developing Type 2 diabetes than those who don't. In addition, raspberries contain ellagic acid, which can reduce insulin resistance, lower blood sugars and counter inflammation.

## *7. Leafy greens*

Greens like cabbage, spinach, chard and broccoli contain plenty of antioxidant compounds (such as lutein and zeaxanthin to help keep eyes healthy), vitamins, and calcium to help maintain bone density. Greens can help to lower high blood pressure, and sulforaphane – a plant compound in broccoli – may help to prevent damage caused to the blood vessels by diabetes.

## *8. Yogurt*

Yogurt and other dairy foods, such as skimmed milk and hard cheese, can promote good bone health, reduce blood pressure and even help the body to burn more fat when you diet. It is thought that the calcium they contain may bind with fat and prevent its absorption. Live or 'probiotic' yogurt can also support immune health and protect against developing Type 2 diabetes.

## *9. Avocados*

Avocados are known for their heart-healthy oleic acid (a type of monounsaturated fat) content, which can improve cholesterol and blood lipids profile, decrease the risk of cardiovascular disease, and may also reduce the risk of developing Type 2 diabetes. The fruits are also rich in potassium, which can help to reduce blood pressure.

## *10. Tomatoes*

Tomatoes, unlike many fruits, have a moderate GI rating of 55 or less and also a low GL because of their low calorie content. Dieticians recommend fresh tomatoes as a fruit that diabetics can eat to satisfy appetite. Regular consumption helps to reduce high blood pressure and research shows it may also help to reduce the risk of cardiovascular disease associated with Type 2 diabetes.

# Crustless courgette and broad bean quiche

This reduced-fat, reduced-calorie quiche has a thin, wholemeal pastry base but no crust around the edges. A perfect summer lunch!

*Calories 412 // Carbohydrates 37.7 g // Sugars 4.7 g // Protein 16.8 g // Fibre 7.1 g // Fat 19.0 g // Saturated fat 7.0 g // Salt 2.5 g*

135 g/4¾ oz wholemeal spelt flour, plus extra for dusting
65 g/2½ oz baking margarine (from a block), chopped
½ tsp salt
2 tbsp water
250 g/9 oz courgettes, cut into 5 mm/¼ inch thick batons
cooking spray, for oiling
100 g/3½ oz broad beans
3 eggs
250 ml/9 fl oz semi-skimmed milk
25 g/1 oz freshly grated Parmesan cheese
2 tbsp chopped fresh mint
pinch of freshly grated nutmeg
125 g/4½ oz baby new potatoes, unpeeled, cut into 1-cm/½-inch dice
salt and pepper
200 g/7 oz mixed salad leaves, to serve

1. Lightly rub together the flour and margarine in a mixing bowl until it resembles fine breadcrumbs. Add the salt and stir, then stir in the water and mix until a ball forms. Wrap the dough in clingfilm and leave to chill in the refrigerator for 30 minutes.

2. Meanwhile, preheat the grill to high. Place the courgettes on a baking sheet and spray with cooking spray to coat, then cook under the preheated grill until slightly charred and soft, turning halfway through. Steam the broad beans until just tender. Combine the eggs, milk, cheese, mint, nutmeg, and salt and pepper to taste in a bowl.

3. Preheat the oven to 190°C/375°F/Gas Mark 5. Remove the pastry from the refrigerator and roll out on a lightly floured surface into a rough round, then cut out a neat round using a 20-cm/8-inch flan dish as a guide.

4. Line the base of the dish with the pastry round and prick all over. Cover with baking paper and baking beans and bake in the preheated oven for 15 minutes. Remove the paper and beans and return to the oven for a further 5 minutes.

5. Spray the inside edges of the flan dish with cooking spray. Spoon the courgettes, broad beans and potatoes evenly into the dish, then gently pour over the egg mixture. Return to the oven and bake for 25 minutes, or until the filling is set but still with some wobble, and the top is golden.

6. Leave to cool in the dish for 15 minutes. Serve warm or cold with the salad leaves.

*Serves: 4 // Preparation time: 25 minutes, plus chilling // Cooking time: 1 hour, plus cooling*

Try to find baby broad beans so that you can enjoy eating them (once you've removed them from their pods) without having to remove the outer pale green skins, which contain much of the fibre in these low-GI vegetables.

*Tip //*

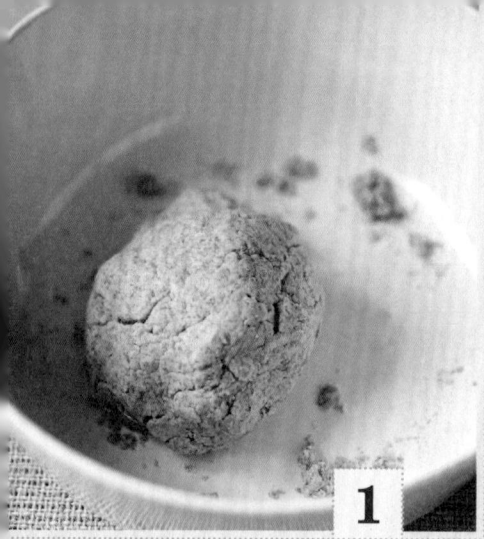
1

2

5

# Avocado, artichoke and almond salad

This beautiful salad is full of healthy ingredients, giving you masses of heart-friendly monounsaturated fats and a huge boost of fibre.

*Calories 364 // Carbohydrates 31.0 g // Sugars 4.1 g // Protein 9.0 g // Fibre 13.4 g // Fat 24.0 g // Saturated fat 3.0 g // Salt 1.4 g*

1 red mini cos lettuce, tough outer leaves discarded
6 canned or bottled artichoke hearts in water, drained and patted dry (about 250 g/9 oz drained weight)
1 small yellow pepper, deseeded and thinly sliced
2 ripe avocados, peeled, stoned and sliced
50 g/1¾ oz lamb's lettuce
40 g/1½ oz flaked almonds
4 radishes, finely chopped
8 dark rye crispbreads, to serve

**Dressing**
3 tbsp balsamic vinegar
1 tbsp olive oil
½ tsp salt
pepper

1. Cut 1.5 cm/⅝ inch from the base of the cos lettuce. Peel off the outer leaves and reserve. Cut the heart lengthways into eight pieces and arrange on a serving platter with the reserved leaves.

2. Halve the artichoke hearts and add to the serving platter with the yellow pepper and avocados.

3. Scatter over the lamb's lettuce, flaked almonds and radishes.

4. To make the dressing, combine the vinegar, oil, salt, and pepper to taste, whisking together thoroughly, then drizzle over the salad. Serve immediately with the crispbreads.

*Serves: 4 // Preparation time: 15 minutes // Cooking time: None*

You can use artichoke hearts that have been canned or bottled in oil or water, but avoid those canned in brine (salted water). You can replace the lamb's lettuce with rocket or watercress for a change.

*Tip //*

# Aubergine paprika salad

This warm salad is a beautiful way to eat aubergines, bringing you smoky flavours, a variety of textures and warm spices all on one plate.

*Calories 475 // Carbohydrates 56.3 g // Sugars 10.6 g // Protein 12.9 g // Fibre 14.1 g // Fat 19.8 g // Saturated fat 2.5 g // Salt 1.7 g*

1. Preheat the grill to high. Cut the aubergines lengthways into 1 cm/½ inch thick slices, brush with oil on both sides and arrange on a grill rack. Add the red pepper pieces. Cook under the preheated grill until the aubergines are charred in patches on the top side; turn over and cook until the aubergines are soft and the red pepper pieces are lightly cooked and slightly brown in places. Remove from the heat but do not switch off the grill. Cut the aubergine slices into large bite-sized pieces and put into a shallow serving dish with the red pepper pieces, chickpeas and red onion.

2. To make the dressing, combine the oil, lemon juice, ground coriander, cumin, paprika and stevia granules with salt and pepper to taste in a small bowl. Add the coriander stalks to the dressing and stir to combine. Spoon the dressing evenly over the salad and stir – it's best to do this while the vegetables are still warm.

3. Meanwhile, lightly toast the pitta breads under the grill.

4. Scatter the salad with the reserved coriander leaves and serve with the pitta breads.

*Serves: 4 // Preparation time: 15 minutes // Cooking time: 20 minutes*

2 aubergines
2 tbsp olive oil
2 red peppers, deseeded and cut into 6 pieces each
400 g/14 oz canned chickpeas, drained and rinsed
1 red onion, finely chopped
4 wholemeal pitta breads, to serve

**Dressing**
3 tbsp olive oil
juice of ½ lemon
1 tsp ground coriander
1 tsp ground cumin
2 tsp smoked paprika
1 tsp stevia granules
small bunch of fresh coriander, leaves removed and reserved and stalks chopped
salt and pepper

Research shows that a diet high in pulses, such as chickpeas, may reduce markers for blood sugars in people with Type 2 diabetes even more successfully than a wholegrain diet.

*Tip //*

1

2

2

1

2

3

# Beef rib-eye steak salad with rocket and Parmesan

This warm salad is extremely quick to make yet bursting with savoury flavours. Rib-eye is one of the tastiest steak cuts you can find.

*Calories 413 // Carbohydrates 20.4 g // Sugars 4.4 g // Protein 36.0 g // Fibre 3.4 g // Fat 17.4 g // Saturated fat 5.3 g // Salt 1.2 g*

4 beef rib-eye steaks, trimmed (about 150 g/5½ oz each)
70 g/2½ oz rocket
70 g/2½ oz watercress
4 tomatoes, cut into wedges
40 g/1½ oz Parmesan cheese shavings, to garnish
4 slices seeded crusty wholemeal bread (about 40 g/1½ oz each), to serve

**Dressing**
3 tbsp balsamic vinegar
juice of ½ lemon
2 tbsp olive oil
1 large garlic clove, crushed
½ tsp salt
pepper

1. Heat a griddle pan until very hot, then add the steaks and cook for 2 minutes. Turn and cook for a further minute for rare to medium-rare. (For medium, cook for 3 minutes, turn and cook for a further 1½ minutes; for well done, cook for 3½ minutes, turn and cook for a further 2 minutes.)

2. Transfer the cooked steaks to a plate, cover and leave to rest for 5–6 minutes. Meanwhile, arrange the rocket, watercress and tomato wedges on serving plates.

3. To make the dressing, combine the vinegar, lemon juice, oil, garlic, salt, and pepper to taste in a bowl.

4. Pour the meat juices that have collected on the steak plate into the dressing. Cut each steak into 1 cm/½ inch thick slices and arrange on the serving plates. Add any juices from the board to the dressing and drizzle the dressing over the salads.

5. Arrange the Parmesan cheese shavings on top of the salads. Serve immediately with the bread.

*Serves: 4 // Preparation time: 10 minutes // Cooking time: 5–8 minutes, plus resting*

Beef is packed with protein to help to stave off hunger. It is also a brilliant source of easily absorbed iron, which is useful because diabetics are more prone to anaemia, and of B vitamins, which can be deficient in diabetics.

*Tip //*

# Smoked mackerel, beetroot and new potato salad

Smoked mackerel and beetroot is one of the best flavour pairings you will find, and this unusual salad is a great way to use this combination.

*Calories 435 // Carbohydrates 26.0 g // Sugars 10.0 g // Protein 24.6 g // Fibre 5.8 g // Fat 26.9 g // Saturated fat 5.2 g // Salt 2.2 g*

500 g/1 lb 2 oz raw beetroot, quartered
2½ tbsp olive oil
2 tbsp balsamic vinegar
300 g/10½ oz baby new potatoes, unpeeled
cooking spray, for coating
70 g/2½ oz rocket
375 g/13 oz smoked mackerel fillets
8 red radishes, thinly sliced
pepper

1. Preheat the oven to 180°C/350°F/Gas Mark 4. Line a roasting tin with aluminium foil. Put the beetroot pieces into a medium-sized bowl.

2. In a small bowl, thoroughly combine the oil and vinegar and spoon a little under half of it into the bowl with the beetroot. Stir well to coat the beetroot pieces, then arrange them on one side of the prepared roasting tin. Tip any dressing remaining in the beetroot bowl back into the small bowl. Bake the beetroot in the preheated oven for 25 minutes.

3. Meanwhile, cook the new potatoes in a saucepan of simmering water until just tender, then arrange on the other side of the roasting tin and spray them with cooking spray to coat. Turn the beetroot and cook for a further 20 minutes, or until the beetroot is cooked through and the outsides of the potatoes are slightly crisp. Leave to cool until just warm.

4. Meanwhile, arrange the rocket on a serving dish and flake the mackerel. Arrange the beetroot and potatoes on the serving dish with the mackerel and sprinkle over the sliced radishes. Combine any juices remaining in the roasting tin with the remaining dressing and drizzle over the salad. Add a grinding of pepper and serve while the beetroot and potatoes are still just warm.

*Serves: 4 // Preparation time: 10 minutes // Cooking time: 45 minutes, plus cooling*

Many people who suffer from diabetes also have high blood pressure, and beetroot has been proven, when eaten regularly, to lower blood pressure convincingly, while mackerel is rich in heart-friendly Omega-3 fats.

*Tip //*

2
3
3

# Lentil and tuna salad

This recipe combines tuna, lentils, tomatoes and red onion for a protein-packed lunch that will help you stay focused all afternoon.

*Calories 225 // Carbohydrates 15.7 g // Sugars 3.2 g // Protein 16.2 g // Fibre 5.9 g // Fat 14.1 g // Saturated fat 1.9 g // Salt 0.5 g*

2 ripe tomatoes
1 small red onion
400 g/14 oz canned brown or green lentils, drained and rinsed
140 g/5 oz canned tuna in water, drained
2 tbsp chopped fresh coriander
pepper

**Dressing**
3 tbsp virgin olive oil
1 tbsp lemon juice
1 tsp wholegrain mustard
1 garlic clove, crushed
½ tsp ground cumin
½ tsp ground coriander

1. Using a sharp knife, deseed the tomatoes and chop them into small dice. Finely chop the red onion.

2. To make the dressing, beat all the dressing ingredients in a small bowl until thoroughly combined. Set aside until required.

3. Mix together the chopped onion, diced tomatoes and drained lentils in a large bowl.

4. Flake the tuna with a fork and stir it into the lentil mixture. Stir in the chopped coriander and mix well.

5. Pour the dressing over the salad and season to taste with pepper. Serve immediately.

*Serves: 4 // Preparation time: 15 minutes // Cooking time: None*

Lentils, particularly the black, brown and green types, are one of the most nutritious foods, and their high levels of soluble and total fibre can help to prevent diverticular disease and other digestive disorders.

*Tip //*

# Little curried crab cakes with avocado salad

Once you've done the preparation, these little crab cakes are easy to put together, and are perfectly complemented by the tangy avocado salad.

*Calories 362 // Carbohydrates 40.0 g // Sugars 3.9 g // Protein 23.7 g // Fibre 7.7 g // Fat 14.0 g // Saturated fat 2.3 g // Salt 1.3 g*

1. Mix together the crabmeat, sweetcorn, breadcrumbs, egg, mayonnaise, yogurt, chives, mustard, curry powder and pepper in a bowl.

2. Using your hands, shape the mixture into eight patties. Spray a non-stick frying pan with cooking spray to coat, then heat to just below medium–hot and add the patties to the pan. Cook the patties for 4 minutes, without turning or moving them.

3. Meanwhile, make the salad. Stone, peel and slice the avocado, then lightly crush it in a bowl. Add the tomato, lime juice, coriander leaves, chilli and spring onions and stir to combine.

4. Spray the tops of the patties with more cooking spray, then use a metal spatula to turn each one over carefully. Cook for a further 3 minutes, or until the crab cakes are golden and piping hot. Serve immediately with the avocado salad.

*Serves: 4 // Preparation time: 20 minutes // Cooking time: 8 minutes*

300 g/10½ oz white crabmeat
150 g/5½ oz canned drained sweetcorn kernels
100 g/3½ oz wholemeal panko breadcrumbs
1 large egg, beaten
1½ tbsp light mayonnaise
1½ tbsp fat-free Greek-style yogurt
2 tbsp snipped fresh chives
2 tsp Dijon mustard
1 tsp curry powder
¼ tsp pepper
cooking spray, for oiling

**Salad**
1 large ripe avocado
1 tomato, finely chopped
juice of ½ lime
small bunch of fresh coriander, leaves only
½ fresh red jalapeño chilli, deseeded and finely chopped
3 spring onions, chopped

*Tip //*

Panko breadcrumbs, originating from Japan, are available in most supermarkets, although you may need to look online for the wholemeal variety. Light and flaky, they make all the difference to the texture of these fish cakes.

1
2
3

# Dinners

# Chilli con carne

One of the most popular family meals – chilli con carne – is transformed into one of the healthiest with just a few sneaky tweaks.

*Calories 622 // Carbohydrates 82.4 g // Sugars 8.4 g // Protein 35.3 g // Fibre 11.3 g // Fat 16.0 g // Saturated fat 3.1 g // Salt 1.6 g*

1 tbsp rapeseed oil
400 g/14 oz fresh lean beef mince (10 per cent fat)
1 large onion, finely chopped
2 celery sticks, chopped
3 garlic cloves, finely chopped
1 large green pepper, deseeded and roughly chopped
400 g/14 oz canned chopped tomatoes
1 tbsp tomato purée
30 g/1 oz chilli pesto
1–2 tsp crushed dried chillies
½ tsp ground coriander
½ tsp ground cumin
1 tsp salt
300 g/10½ oz brown basmati rice
200 g/7 oz mushrooms, sliced
400 g/14 oz canned red kidney beans, drained and rinsed
pepper
2 tbsp chopped fresh flat-leaf parsley, to garnish

1. Heat the oil in a large non-stick frying pan over a medium–high heat. Add the beef and cook, stirring occasionally, for a few minutes, until browned all over.

2. Push the beef to the side of the pan, then add the onion, celery and garlic. Reduce the heat to medium–low, cover and cook for 5 minutes, until the vegetables are soft but not browned.

3. Stir in the green pepper, tomatoes, tomato purée, pesto, chillies, ground coriander, cumin, ½ teaspoon of the salt, and pepper to taste. Bring to a simmer, reduce the heat to very low, then re-cover and cook for 25 minutes.

4. Meanwhile, cook the rice with the remaining salt according to the packet instructions until tender, then drain.

5. Add the mushrooms and kidney beans to the beef mixture and stir. Bring back to a simmer and cook for a further 5 minutes. Garnish the chilli with the parsley and serve immediately with the rice.

*Serves: 4 // Preparation time: 15–20 minutes // Cooking time: 45 minutes*

Beef mince is very variable in the amount of fat it contains – look for the type that has around 10 per cent fat. Any higher and it will be too high in saturates; any lower and the meat could taste rather tough and dry.

*Tip //*

1
2
4

# Spaghetti and meatballs

Packed with warming flavours and textures, this is a hearty low-cost meal idea that is perfect for chilly autumn or winter evenings.

*Calories 585 // Carbohydrates 74.5 g // Sugars 11.7 g // Protein 36.4 g // Fibre 8.0 g // Fat 16.4 g // Saturated fat 4.1 g // Salt 1.5 g*

50 g/1¾ oz fresh white breadcrumbs
50 ml/1¾ fl oz skimmed milk
400 g/14 oz fresh lean pork mince (10 per cent fat)
1 onion, very finely chopped
2 garlic cloves, crushed
2 tbsp chopped fresh parsley
2 tsp crushed fennel seeds
1 tbsp olive oil
300 g/10½ oz dried wholegrain spelt spaghetti or wholemeal spaghetti
salt and pepper
fresh basil leaves, to garnish

**Sauce**

125 g/4½ oz courgettes, coarsely grated
3 garlic cloves, finely grated
800 g/1 lb 12 oz canned chopped tomatoes
1 tbsp tomato purée
1 tsp maple syrup
1 tsp red wine vinegar

1. Mix the breadcrumbs with the milk and leave to soak for a few minutes, then transfer to a mixing bowl and add the pork, onion, garlic, parsley, fennel seeds, and salt and pepper to taste. Combine well, then shape into 16 meatballs, transferring each to a plate as you make them.

2. Heat the oil in a large frying pan with a lid. Add the meatballs and cook, uncovered, over a medium–high heat for a few minutes, turning occasionally, until slightly brown. Transfer to a plate with a slotted spoon, cover and set aside.

3. To make the sauce, reduce the heat to medium and add the grated courgettes to the frying pan. Cook for 1–2 minutes, then add the garlic and cook for a few seconds.

4. Add the tomatoes, tomato purée, maple syrup and vinegar, mix thoroughly and bring to a gentle simmer. Cover and cook for 15 minutes, then remove the lid and cook, stirring occasionally, for a further 10 minutes.

5. Return the meatballs to the pan and stir to coat in the sauce, then cook for a further 10 minutes, or until about half the liquid has evaporated and you have a rich sauce.

6. Meanwhile, bring a large saucepan of very lightly salted water to the boil. Add the spaghetti and cook for 8–10 minutes, until tender but still firm to the bite. Drain the spaghetti, transfer to a serving platter and spoon the tomato sauce and meatballs on top. Garnish with basil leaves and serve immediately.

*Serves: 4 // Preparation time: 25–30 minutes // Cooking time: 50 minutes*

If you haven't ever had spelt spaghetti, do give it a try. It is now widely available and has a delicious nutty flavour and a texture similar to wholemeal spaghetti.

*Tip //*

# Chinese marinated flank steak with noodles

Flank steak is an underused cut of beef that lends itself very well to Asian flavours. It can be cooked quickly, just like more expensive cuts of steak.

*Calories 533 // Carbohydrates 60.0 g // Sugars 4.0g // Protein 38.8 g // Fibre 6.0 g // Fat 16.4 g // Saturated fat 4.8 g // Salt 0.9 g*

1. To make the marinade, combine all the ingredients in a small bowl.

2. Put the steak in a non-metallic shallow bowl just large enough to fit it, pour over the marinade, then cover with clingfilm. Leave to stand at room temperature for at least 1 hour.

3. Preheat a large frying pan over a high heat. Remove the steak from the marinade (reserving the marinade), add to the pan and cook for 3 minutes on each side. Remove the pan from the heat, take the steak out of the pan and cut it into thick strips, slicing against the grain. Set aside on a warmed plate to rest and keep warm.

4. Cook or soak the noodles according to the packet instructions and drain.

5. Add the red pepper and spring onions to the frying pan with the oil and stir-fry over a high heat for 2 minutes. Reduce the heat to medium, add the reserved marinade to the pan and stir for 1 minute, then add the noodles and beansprouts to the pan and stir for a further minute.

6. Serve the noodle mixture with the pieces of steak on top, drizzled with any juices from the plate.

*Serves: 4 // Preparation time: 15 minutes, plus marinating // Cooking time: 20 minutes*

500 g/1 lb 2 oz thick flank steak, fat trimmed
275 g/9¾ oz dried wholemeal noodles
1 large red pepper, deseeded and thinly sliced
6 spring onions, sliced diagonally
2 tsp sesame oil
150 g/5½ oz fresh beansprouts

**Marinade**
4 tsp sesame oil
2 tbsp rice wine vinegar
4 garlic cloves, crushed
1 tbsp finely chopped ginger
1 fresh red jalapeño chilli, sliced
1 tbsp teriyaki marinating sauce
1 tbsp light soy sauce

Adding plenty of spices, such as chilli, garlic and ginger, to your diet is a healthy thing to do as they contain a variety of antioxidant compounds that can help to reduce the risk of heart disease.

*Tip //*

1
2
5

1
2
3

# Turkey paprika tacos

Turkey makes a great change from chicken in almost any dish and its somewhat richer flavour lends itself well to Mexican-style meals like this.

*Calories 321 // Carbohydrates 31.4 g // Sugars 5.3 g // Protein 29.7 g // Fibre 6.7 g // Fat 8.0 g // Saturated fat 4.1 g // Salt 1.0 g*

300 g/10½ oz skinless, boneless turkey breasts, cut into strips
2 garlic cloves, crushed
2 tsp smoked paprika
juice of ½ lime
1 red onion, chopped
1 tomato, chopped
100 g/3½ oz cooked black beans
100 g/3½ oz crisp lettuce, shredded
4 wholemeal tortillas
40 g/1½ oz reduced-fat Cheddar cheese, grated
2 tsp hot pepper sauce
100 g/3½ oz reduced-fat soured cream

1. Put the turkey strips in a non-metallic shallow bowl. Stir in the garlic with the paprika and lime juice. Cover and leave to marinate for 30 minutes.

2. Meanwhile, combine the onion, tomato, beans and lettuce in a bowl.

3. Preheat the grill to medium–hot. Line a baking tray with aluminium foil. Put the turkey strips on the prepared baking tray and cook under the preheated grill for about 6 minutes, turning once, until golden and cooked through. Set aside.

4. Heat the tortillas under the grill until slightly golden and crisp. Divide the turkey and the bean mixture evenly between the tortillas, arranging them on one half of the tortilla only. Scatter over the cheese and drizzle with the hot pepper sauce and soured cream. Fold the tacos to serve.

*Serves: 4 // Preparation time: 15 minutes, plus marinating // Cooking time: 8 minutes*

Black beans are a rich source of resistant starch. You can buy dried black beans and soak and cook them yourself, or choose beans that are canned or boxed in water (not brine).

*Tip //*

# Chicken escalopes with cherry tomatoes

These succulent chicken escalopes make a lovely light supper and are ideal for days when you have had a higher-carbohydrate lunch.

*Calories 342 // Carbohydrates 28.0 g // Sugars 3.9 g // Protein 32.7 g // Fibre 2.1 g // Fat 12.0 g // Saturated fat 2.1 g // Salt 0.7 g*

3 skinless, boneless chicken breasts, about 500 g/1 lb 2 oz total weight
1 egg, beaten
100 g/3½ oz wholemeal panko breadcrumbs
1 tsp dried thyme
1 tsp dried oregano
2 tbsp groundnut oil
400 g/14 oz cherry tomatoes on the vine
200 g/7 oz baby leaf salad
1 tbsp balsamic vinegar

1. Diagonally slice each chicken breast in four lengthways to make 12 escalopes. Place each escalope on a chopping board and pound it a few times with a rolling pin to a thickness of about 1 cm/½ inch.

2. Put the beaten egg in a shallow dish and put the breadcrumbs in a separate shallow dish. Stir the thyme and oregano into the breadcrumbs.

3. Coat each escalope in egg, then hold it above the egg dish to allow the excess to drip off. Dip into the breadcrumb mixture, turning to coat, then transfer to a large plate.

4. Heat the oil in a large, non-stick frying pan. Add the escalopes, in batches, and cook over a medium heat for about 4 minutes on each side, until the breadcrumbs are golden and the escalopes are cooked all the way through.

5. Meanwhile, preheat the grill and grill the tomatoes on the vine until warmed through but not collapsed.

6. Serve the escalopes with the grilled tomatoes and the baby leaf salad, drizzled with the vinegar.

*Serves: 4 // Preparation time: 15 minutes // Cooking time: 25 minutes*

Balsamic vinegar is extremely useful as a quick and easy salad dressing. Each tablespoon contains just 14 calories and it is free from fat and salt. It is worth buying a more expensive aged balsamic for its taste and texture.

*Tip //*

1
3
4

# Eating out

Of course you want a special meal if you're eating out at a great restaurant or your favourite café, especially if you don't do it very often. The good news is that there's usually plenty on any menu that you can eat without having to feel guilty the next day. However, statistics show that food eaten out contains on average at least 50 per cent more fat and calories than the meals you eat at home, so it pays to use a few tips to minimise the potential for dietary disaster.

* If you're eating in a restaurant, decide beforehand whether you're going to have a starter or a dessert along with your main course, rather than both.

* If possible, check out the menu before you go to a restaurant and try to decide what you're going to eat. It will often save you from making less wise choices on the spur of the moment.

* If you are having more than one course, try to balance out the courses in the same way that you would balance a meal at home – for example, one high-carbohydrate course balances one high-protein course, or one low-fat course balances one high-fat course.

* Add as many vegetables or as much salad to your plate as you can. If you're having a main with a rich sauce, try to accompany it with plainly cooked vegetables.

* Try to avoid 'white' carbohydrates (such as white bread, white rice and white pasta), instead choosing wholemeal or wholegrain versions.

* Rather than having a side of potatoes, see if the restaurant will serve you lower-GI sweet potatoes; a protein-rich grain (such as quinoa); or mashed pulses (such as a white bean purée), which have a great balance of protein and carbohydrates.

* Try to pick an eating establishment where you aren't kept waiting a long time to begin eating, which may tempt you to fill up on the bread basket and/or drink alcohol to pass the time.

* If you have to watch your weight, it is best to avoid restaurants and cafés that offer help-yourself buffets and/or 'all-you-can-eat' deals. Research shows that people continue to eat at this type of venue even when they are full.

* Some of the dishes most likely to be very high in calories and fat include pastry dishes; many meat and korma dishes at Indian and Thai restaurants; rich pasta dishes, such as lasagne and pasta carbonara, and most pizzas at Italian restaurants; and French dishes à la meunière and hearty cassoulets with pork, lamb or sausages.

* Some dishes most likely to be lower in calories and fat include lean steak, venison or chicken; Japanese food; vegetable and seafood stir-fries; grilled or baked fish; non-creamy vegetable soups or broths; and meat, poultry, seafood and vegetable skewers.

1
2
5

# Chicken chow mein

This popular Chinese dish is simple to make and, once you've prepared your ingredients, it can be on the table in just over 10 minutes.

*Calories 469 // Carbohydrates 65.0 g // Sugars 9.4 g // Protein 29.0 g // Fibre 7.2 g // Fat 9.6 g // Saturated fat 1.4 g // Salt 2.0 g*

1. To make the sauce, crush the garlic with the flat of a large knife. Put the garlic and ginger in a small bowl with the tomato ketchup, oyster sauce, soy sauce, stock and sesame oil. Stir well to combine and set aside.

2. Bring a large saucepan of water to the boil, add the noodles and cook for 4 minutes, or according to the packet instructions. Meanwhile, put the chicken in a bowl, add the soy sauce and toss to coat.

3. Drain the noodles and set aside. Heat half the groundnut oil in a wok or large, deep frying pan until very hot, then stir in the chicken and cook for 2–3 minutes. Remove from the wok and set aside.

4. Add the orange pepper, spring onions, carrots, broccoli, mangetout and the remaining groundnut oil to the wok and stir for 1–2 minutes, until coloured and soft. Add the sauce, stir again and leave it to bubble up for 1–2 minutes.

5. Return the chicken to the wok and add the mushrooms and beansprouts, stirring for a further minute. Stir in the noodles to warm through and serve immediately.

*Serves: 4 // Preparation time: 25 minutes // Cooking time: 15–18 minutes*

250 g/9 oz dried wholemeal noodles
2 skinless, boneless chicken breasts, about 300 g/10½ oz total weight, cut into 3-cm/1¼-inch strips
1 tbsp reduced-salt soy sauce
1 tbsp groundnut oil
1 large orange pepper, deseeded and thinly sliced
8 spring onions, diagonally sliced
100 g/3½ oz carrots, thinly sliced
100 g/3½ oz broccoli, cut into small florets
75 g/2¾ oz mangetout
100 g/3½ oz oriental mushrooms, such as shiitake, sliced if large
300 g/10½ oz fresh beansprouts

**Sauce**
3 garlic cloves
2.5-cm/1-inch piece fresh ginger, finely chopped
2 tbsp reduced-salt tomato ketchup
1 tbsp oyster sauce
1 tbsp reduced-salt soy sauce
100 ml/3½ fl oz reduced-salt chicken stock
1 tbsp sesame oil

Recent research links oriental mushrooms with protection from cardiovascular disease.

*Tip //*

# Chicken and prawn jambalaya

The name sounds fun and cheerful, and so is the look and taste of this dish with its riot of colours, flavours and textures.

*Calories 548 // Carbohydrates 52.0 g // Sugars 7.0 g // Protein 44.7 g // Fibre 5.2 g // Fat 17.6 g // Saturated fat 3.8 g // Salt 1.6 g*

1 tbsp rapeseed oil
4 large skinless, boneless chicken thighs, each cut into 3 pieces (500 g/1 lb 2 oz total weight)
30 g/1 oz chorizo, chopped
1 onion, finely chopped
2 celery sticks, chopped
1 green pepper, deseeded and chopped
1 red pepper, deseeded and chopped
2 garlic cloves, crushed
1 fresh green chilli, deseeded and finely chopped
1 fresh red chilli, deseeded and finely chopped
300 g/10½ oz canned chopped tomatoes
1 tbsp chilli pesto
500 ml/18 fl oz reduced-salt chicken stock
200 g/7 oz brown basmati rice
200 g/7 oz raw prawns, peeled and deveined
pepper
2 tbsp chopped fresh flat-leaf parsley, to garnish

1. Heat the oil in a large frying pan with a lid over medium–high heat, then add the chicken and cook, uncovered, for 1–2 minutes. Add the chorizo and cook for a further minute, stirring, until it begins to release its oils. Using a slotted spoon, remove the chicken and chorizo from the pan and set aside.

2. Reduce the heat to medium–low, stir the onion, celery, green pepper and red pepper into the pan and cook for 5–10 minutes, until soft, adding a little of the stock if the pan gets dry.

3. Add the garlic to the pan with the chillies. Cook for 1 minute, then stir in the tomatoes, pesto, pepper to taste and a little of the stock and cook for a further minute.

4. Stir in most of the remaining stock and the rice. Bring to a simmer, return the chicken and chorizo to the pan and cook, covered and without stirring, for 16 minutes. Lift the lid to check that the dish isn't too dry. If it is, stir in the remaining stock and/or a little boiling water, cover and cook for a further 4 minutes. If it is too wet, remove the lid for the rest of the cooking time. Stir in the prawns to cook through for the last 3 minutes of the cooking time. The jambalaya is ready when the rice has absorbed almost all of the stock and is tender, and the chicken, prawns and vegetables are cooked through.

5. Garnish with parsley and serve immediately.

*Serves: 4 // Preparation time: 25 minutes // Cooking time: 35–40 minutes*

Basmati rice has a lower GI rating than other types of rice, while brown rice contains more fibre and nutrients than white rice.

*Tip //*

1
3
4

# Fish and chips

This version of the classic fish and chips tastes fantastic and is much lower in calories, fat and salt because it is all cooked in the oven.

*Calories 412 // Carbohydrates 54.9 g // Sugars 7.2 g // Protein 35.2 g // Fibre 8.4 g // Fat 9.8 g // Saturated fat 1.6 g // Salt 1.5 g*

1 egg, beaten
60 g/2¼ oz dried wholemeal breadcrumbs
2 tsp low-salt season-all
4 skinless cod loin fillets, about 140 g/5 oz each
600 g/1 lb 5 oz large floury potatoes, scrubbed and cut into chunky chips
1 tsp garam masala
1 tsp paprika
½ tsp salt
1 tbsp groundnut oil
cooking spray, for oiling
320 g/11 oz frozen peas

**Sauce**
2 tbsp light mayonnaise
1 tbsp fat-free Greek-style yogurt
2 tsp lemon juice

1. Preheat the oven to 200°C/400°F/Gas Mark 6. Put the beaten egg in a shallow dish. Put the breadcrumbs in a separate shallow dish and thoroughly stir in the season-all. Dry the fish fillets on kitchen paper.

2. Dry the potato chips on kitchen paper. Put them into a large bowl and stir in the garam masala, paprika, salt and oil. Combine thoroughly, then spread out the chips on a baking tray. Bake on the top shelf of the preheated oven for 5 minutes.

3. Meanwhile, coat each fish fillet first in the beaten egg, allowing any excess to drip back into the dish, and then in the breadcrumbs. Place them on a separate baking tray lined with baking paper and spray thoroughly with cooking spray.

4. Put the fish in the oven on the shelf beneath the chips and bake for 5 minutes. Turn the chips over with a large spatula and return to the oven for a further 10 minutes, or until the chips are crisp on the outside and soft in the centre and the fish is cooked through.

5. Meanwhile, bring a small saucepan of water to the boil, add the peas and cook for 5 minutes, or until tender. Drain and keep warm.

6. To make the sauce, combine the mayonnaise, yogurt and lemon juice in a small bowl.

7. Serve the fish and chips immediately with the peas and sauce.

*Serves: 4 // Preparation time: 20 minutes // Cooking time: 20 minutes*

When choosing potatoes for chips, try to get a variety that will be soft and floury in the centre and crisp and golden on the outside – some of the best are Maris Piper, King Edward and Albert Bartlett Rooster.

*Tip //*

2

3

5

1
2
4

# Monkfish, mushroom and red pepper skewers

Monkfish is firm, meaty and a perfect fish for kebabs. It also goes extremely well with bacon, so this dish is bound to become a favourite.

*Calories 429 // Carbohydrates 41.0 g // Sugars 6.0 g // Protein 40.7 g // Fibre 3.8 g // Fat 12.2 g // Saturated fat 2.6 g // Salt 1.7 g*

160 g/5¾ oz brown basmati rice
400 g/14 oz small chestnut mushrooms, stalks removed
650 g/1 lb 7 oz monkfish tail fillet, cut into 2.5-cm/1-inch cubes
1 large red pepper, deseeded and cut into 2.5-cm/1-inch squares
3 low-salt lean back bacon rashers, trimmed and cut into 2.5-cm/1-inch squares
1½ tbsp olive oil
salt
fresh coriander sprigs, to garnish

**Sauce**
5 pieces semi-sundried tomato, finely chopped
1 tbsp lemon juice
1 large tomato, peeled and finely chopped
1 heaped tsp smoked paprika
1 garlic clove, crushed

1. Place the rice in a saucepan of very lightly salted water, then cover and cook over a low heat for 20 minutes, or until tender.

2. Meanwhile, cut any large mushrooms in half. Thread the fish, mushrooms, red pepper and bacon evenly onto four metal skewers.

3. Preheat the grill and brush the kebabs with the oil. Place the kebabs on a rack under the preheated grill and cook for about 4 minutes on each side, or until the fish and bacon are cooked through and the vegetables are tender.

4. To make the sauce, combine the sun-dried tomatoes, lemon juice, tomato, paprika and garlic in a small bowl.

5. Drain the rice. Serve the kebabs with the rice and a spoonful of the sauce. Garnish with coriander sprigs.

*Serves: 4 // Preparation time: 15 minutes // Cooking time: 25 minutes*

If you can't get hold of monkfish, you could try using swordfish, or even hake or snapper instead. All these fish are high in protein and very low in fat and calories.

*Tip //*

# Salmon ramen

In this Asian-inspired dish, heart-healthy salmon is given a sticky teriyaki glaze and served in an aromatic broth with noodles and vegetables.

*Calories 397 // Carbohydrates 32.7 g // Sugars 4.2 g // Protein 34.2 g // Fibre 2.5 g // Fat 12.4 g // Saturated fat 2.3 g // Salt 3.0 g*

1. Preheat the grill to high. Put the stock in a saucepan, add the garlic clove and soy sauce and bring to the boil.

2. Mix together the ingredients for the glaze and brush one surface of each salmon fillet with the glaze. Lightly brush the grill rack with the oil and cook the salmon under the preheated grill for 4 minutes on one side only. The flesh should flake easily and the centre should remain a bright pink. Remove the fish from the grill and set aside.

3. Cook the noodles according to the packet instructions. Drain and set aside.

4. Remove the garlic from the stock, then bring the stock back to the boil. Drop in the spinach leaves and spring onions and cook until the leaves are just wilted. Use a slotted spoon to remove the spinach and spring onions from the pan and divide them among warmed bowls. Divide the noodles between the bowls, then add a salmon fillet to each. Carefully pour the boiling stock into each bowl.

5. Scatter over the beansprouts, chilli slices and coriander sprigs and serve immediately.

*Serves: 4 // Preparation time: 15–20 minutes // Cooking time: 20 minutes*

1 litre/1¾ pints reduced-salt vegetable stock
1 large garlic clove
½ tsp light soy sauce
4 skinless salmon fillets, about 140 g/5 oz each
½ tbsp groundnut oil
140 g/5 oz dried fine egg noodles or ramen noodles
100 g/3½ oz baby spinach leaves
4 spring onions, chopped

**Glaze**
2½ tbsp sake
2½ tbsp light soy sauce
2 tbsp mirin or sweet sherry
1 tsp maple syrup
½ garlic clove, very finely chopped
5-mm/¼-inch piece fresh ginger, very finely chopped

**To serve**
100 g/3½ oz fresh beansprouts
1 fresh green chilli, deseeded and sliced
fresh coriander sprigs

Salmon is rich in the health-promoting fatty acid DHA (short for docosahexaenoic acid), which can help to reduce the health complications of diabetes.

*Tip //*

# Tuna and broccoli pasta bake

Many tuna pasta bake recipes are very high in saturates, salt and calories. Not so this version, which is also high in fibre and protein.

*Calories 553 // Carbohydrates 54.0 g // Sugars 10.1 g //Protein 32.0 g // Fibre 8.1 g // Fat 19.7 g // Saturated fat 5.7 g // Salt 1.6 g*

1. Preheat the oven to 190°C/375°F/Gas Mark 5. Bring a large saucepan of very lightly salted water to the boil, then add the pasta and cook for 12 minutes, or until tender but still firm to the bite. Drain.

2. Meanwhile, steam the broccoli florets until just tender. Flake the tuna.

3. Put the tuna oil, pesto and passata in a saucepan and cook, stirring, over a medium–high heat for 1–2 minutes, until warmed through.

4. Tip the cooked pasta into a shallow ovenproof dish along with the sauce, broccoli, cherry tomatoes and tuna. Stir gently to make sure all the pasta is well covered.

5. Dot the top with the soft cheese, then sprinkle over the Cheddar cheese and breadcrumbs. Bake in the preheated oven for 20 minutes, or until heated through and the cheese is golden and melted. Serve immediately with the salad leaves.

*Serves: 4 // Preparation time: 15 minutes // Cooking time: 35 minutes*

240 g/8½ oz dried wholemeal penne pasta
200 g/7 oz broccoli florets
320 g/11 oz canned tuna steak in olive oil, drained and 1½ tbsp of the oil reserved
1 tbsp red pesto
350 g/12 oz passata with onions and garlic
6 cherry tomatoes, halved
100 g/3½ oz reduced-fat soft cheese
50 g/1¾ oz reduced-fat Cheddar cheese, grated
25 g/1 oz fresh wholemeal breadcrumbs
salt
200 g/7 oz mixed salad leaves, to serve

Broccoli has anti-inflammatory properties, and is a very rich source of vitamin C. Steamed broccoli has a more marked ability to lower blood cholesterol than broccoli cooked in any other way.

*Tip //*

1
3
5

1

3

4

# Lentil burgers

The whole family – whether vegetarian or not – will enjoy these burgers made from tasty Puy lentils threaded through with deep green spinach.

*Calories 363 // Carbohydrates 47.5 g // Sugars 4.4 g // Protein 18.0 g // Fibre 11.2 g // Fat 12.6 g // Saturated fat 2.1 g // Salt 2.2 g*

1. Bring a small saucepan of lightly salted water to the boil, add the potatoes and cook for 10 minutes, until soft. Drain thoroughly, then return to the hob with the heat turned off. The residual heat will dry out any remaining moisture – shake the pan to help.

2. Meanwhile, put the spinach in a microwaveable bowl and microwave at full power (850 watts) for 1½ minutes, or until thoroughly wilted. Transfer to a sieve and push all the moisture out using the end of a rolling pin or a pestle. Dry again on strong kitchen paper.

3. Put the potatoes, lentils, onion, mushrooms, 1 teaspoon of salt, and pepper to taste in a food processor and process for 1 minute to a semi-smooth mixture with some texture. Stir the spinach, parsley and thyme into the mixture by hand, then stir in the egg. Shape into four large 1 cm/½ inch thick burgers.

4. Heat the oil in a large, non-stick frying pan. Add the burgers and cook, in batches if necessary, over a medium heat for 3 minutes on each side. You may need to reduce the heat to low for the last minute of cooking on either side to prevent the burgers from over-browning.

5. Split the burger buns and spread them with the mayonnaise. Place the burgers in the buns with the tomato slices and serve immediately with the salad leaves on the side.

*Serves: 4 // Preparation time: 20 minutes // Cooking time: 25 minutes*

100 g/3½ oz floury potatoes, cut into 2-cm/¾-inch cubes
100 g/3½ oz baby spinach leaves
250 g/9 oz cooked Puy lentils
1 onion, roughly chopped
100 g/3½ oz chestnut mushrooms, roughly chopped
1 heaped tbsp chopped fresh parsley
2 tsp fresh thyme leaves
1 small egg, beaten
1½ tbsp extra virgin rapeseed oil
1 tsp salt
pepper

**To serve**

4 wholemeal burger buns, about 50 g/1¾ oz each
40 g/1½ oz light mayonnaise
1 large tomato, sliced
240 g/8½ oz mixed salad leaves

When choosing a bag of ready-mixed salad leaves to serve with this burger, try to buy one with a good variety of deep-coloured leaves in it – dark green, purple or red, for example – as these leaves will contain the most nutrients and antioxidants.

*Tip //*

# Butternut squash and spinach curry

Squash makes a delightful main ingredient for a curry and goes particularly well with coconut milk in this easy dinner.

*Calories 486 // Carbohydrates 80.2 g // Sugars 8.8 g // Protein 11.7 g // Fibre 10.6 g // Fat 14.1 g // Saturated fat 5.9 g // Salt 1.7 g*

*Tip //*

Butternut and other winter squashes are a very useful food for diabetics as they contain the compound inositol and the fibre pectin, both of which help to regulate blood sugars and insulin production.

1 tbsp groundnut oil
1 large onion, sliced
2 garlic cloves, crushed
3-cm/1¼-inch piece fresh ginger, finely chopped
75 g/2¾ oz korma curry paste
1 small butternut squash, peeled, deseeded and cut into bite-sized cubes (about 425 g/15 oz prepared weight)
400 g/14 oz canned chickpeas, drained and rinsed
300 ml/10 fl oz light coconut milk
500 ml/18 fl oz water
½ tsp salt
200 g/7 oz brown basmati rice
200 g/7 oz fresh spinach leaves
large handful of fresh coriander leaves

1. Heat the oil in a large saucepan, then add the onion and cook over a medium–low heat for 5 minutes, or until soft. Add the garlic and ginger and cook, stirring, for 1 minute.

2. Increase the heat to medium–high, add the curry paste and cook for 2 minutes. Add the squash, chickpeas and coconut milk, stir well and bring to a simmer. Reduce the heat to low and simmer for 25 minutes, or until the squash is tender.

3. Meanwhile, put the water into a saucepan with the salt, cover and bring to a simmer. Add the rice and simmer for 25 minutes, or until the rice is tender and the water has been absorbed.

4. Stir the spinach into the curry and leave it to wilt for 1 minute. Scatter the coriander leaves over the curry and serve immediately with the rice.

*Serves: 4 // Preparation time: 15–20 minutes // Cooking time: 35–40 minutes*

# Winter root vegetable tagine

This spicy casserole is a good option for a meat-free meal. Its huge fibre content makes it extremely satisfying, and it is also low in saturates.

*Calories 458 // Carbohydrates 81 g // Sugars 11.5 g // Protein 13.7 g // Fibre 11.6 g // Fat 9g // Saturated fat 1.4 g // Salt 2.1 g*

1 tbsp olive oil
2 red onions, thickly sliced
2 large garlic cloves, crushed
2 tbsp tomato purée
2 tbsp harissa paste
2 carrots, cut into thick batons
100 g/3½ oz potatoes, cut into 3-cm/1¼-inch chunks
200 g/7 oz sweet potatoes, cut into 3-cm/1¼-inch chunks
200 g/7 oz swede, cut into 15 mm/⅝ inch thick rounds, then quartered
600 ml/1 pint reduced-salt vegetable stock
150 g/5½ oz cooked butter beans or cannellini beans
300 g/10½ oz canned chopped tomatoes
pinch of salt (optional)
200 g/7 oz wholewheat couscous
large handful of fresh flat-leaf parsley, chopped
pepper

1. Heat the oil in a flameproof casserole, add the onions and cook over a medium–low heat for 5 minutes, or until soft and transparent. Add the garlic, tomato purée and harissa paste and cook, stirring, for 1 minute.

2. Add the carrots, potatoes, sweet potatoes and swede. Pour in the stock, add pepper to taste and bring to a simmer. Cover and cook for 30 minutes, or until the vegetables are almost soft, stirring once halfway through.

3. Stir in the beans and tomatoes and cook for a further 15 minutes. Press some of the beans into the side of the casserole dish to break them up and thicken the sauce. Check the seasoning, adding more pepper to taste and a pinch of salt, if using.

4. Meanwhile, prepare the couscous according to the packet instructions.

5. Scatter the parsley over the tagine and serve immediately with the couscous.

*Serves: 4 // Preparation time: 25 minutes // Cooking time: 1 hour*

Orange and yellow vegetables, such as carrots, sweet potatoes and swede, are rich in beta-carotene, which can help to reduce the risk of coronary heart disease. Sweet potatoes have a lower GI rating than standard potatoes.

*Tip //*

# Sides and snacks

# Sweet potato fries

Orange-fleshed sweet potatoes make a simple and tasty alternative to regular chips in this delicious, low-fat recipe.

*Calories 183 // Carbohydrates 35.7 g // Sugars 7.0 g // Protein 2.9 g // Fibre 5.3 g // Fat 3.5 g // Saturated fat 0.5 g // Salt 1.0 g*

*Tip //*

Sweet potatoes are worth choosing over regular potatoes at least some of the time because they offer several additional benefits for your health. They are richer in vitamins C and A and they also contain more fibre.

1 tbsp groundnut oil
4 sweet potatoes, about 175 g/6 oz each
½ tsp salt
½ tsp ground cumin
¼ tsp cayenne pepper

1. Preheat the oven to 230°C/450°F/Gas Mark 8. Brush a large baking tray with a little of the oil.

2. Peel the sweet potatoes and slice into 5 mm/¼ inch thick spears about 7.5 cm/3 inches long. Spread the sweet potatoes on the prepared baking tray, pour over the remaining oil and toss to coat.

3. In a small bowl, combine the salt, cumin and cayenne pepper. Sprinkle the spice mixture evenly over the sweet potatoes and then toss again.

4. Spread the sweet potatoes out into a single layer and bake in the preheated oven for about 15–20 minutes, or until cooked through and lightly coloured. Serve hot.

*Serves: 4 // Preparation time: 10 minutes // Cooking time: 15–20 minutes*

# Celeriac and new potato smash

Try this rustic mash as an accompaniment to a food high in protein, such as lean venison sausages, roast chicken or lamb steaks.

*Calories 144 // Carbohydrates 25.0 g // Sugars 2.8 g // Protein 3.2 g // Fibre 4.2 g // Fat 3.9 g // Saturated fat 0.6 g // Salt 0.9 g*

*Tip //*

Although plain celeriac has a fairly high GI rating, the addition of the skin-on new potatoes and the oil, and the fact that you don't completely mash the vegetables means that this dish has a medium glycaemic load overall.

1 small celeriac, about 400 g/14 oz, peeled and cut into 2-cm/¾-inch chunks
400 g/14 oz new potatoes, scrubbed and cut into 2-cm/¾-inch chunks
2 garlic cloves, crushed
1 tbsp olive oil
100 ml/3½ fl oz reduced-salt vegetable stock
½ tsp celery salt
2 tsp fresh thyme leaves
1 tbsp chopped fresh flat-leaf parsley
pepper

1. Put the celeriac into a large frying pan over a medium–high heat. Add the potatoes, garlic and oil and stir. Fry for 3–4 minutes, stirring occasionally, until the vegetables are lightly coloured.

2. Pour in the stock, add the celery salt, thyme, and pepper to taste and bring to a simmer. Cover and braise the vegetables for 20 minutes, adding a little water if they begin to look dry.

3. Using a potato masher, bash the vegetables in the pan – don't mash them, just break them down into smallish pieces. Sprinkle over the parsley, stir and serve immediately.

*Serves: 4 // Preparation time: 15 minutes // Cooking time: 25 minutes*

1
2
3

1

2

3

# Onion and root vegetable winter roast

For a healthy alternative to roast potatoes, this mixed vegetable traybake complements any roast meat, particularly beef and chicken.

*Calories 252 // Carbohydrates 50.6 g // Sugars 11.0 g // Protein 4.7 g // Fibre 8.1 g // Fat 3.8 g // Saturated fat 0.2 g // Salt 1.3 g*

2 red onions, about 200 g/7 oz total weight, quartered
6 small shallots
200 g/7 oz parsnips, cut into thick sticks
200 g/7 oz sweet potatoes, cut into thick sticks
200 g/7 oz yams, cut into thick sticks
150 g/5½ oz Jerusalem artichokes, scrubbed and halved
8 large garlic cloves, unpeeled
1 tbsp rapeseed oil
1 tbsp lemon juice
1 tsp salt
pepper

1. Preheat the oven to 190°C/375°F/Gas Mark 5. Place the onions and shallots in a roasting tin.

2. Add the parsnips, sweet potatoes, yams, Jerusalem artichokes and garlic to the roasting tin.

3. Pour in the oil and lemon juice. Add the salt and pepper to taste, then stir so that the vegetables are thoroughly coated with the oil and lemon juice.

4. Bake in the preheated oven for 20 minutes. Turn the vegetables with a spatula and bake for a further 25 minutes, or until they are golden and cooked through. The garlic cloves should be meltingly soft inside – if you like, press the contents of each garlic clove out and into the pan juices and stir in with a little water. Serve immediately.

*Serves: 4 // Preparation time: 15 minutes // Cooking time: 45 minutes*

Onions and many root vegetables are surprisingly high in sugars, but their high fibre content means that these sugars will not cause a sudden spike in your blood sugars. Yams are high in resistant starch.

*Tip //*

# Avocado, tomato, basil and red onion salad

This simple salad would be lovely served with almost anything. It could also be turned into a lunch dish with the addition of buffalo mozzarella.

*Calories 196 // Carbohydrates 10.0 g // Sugars 2.3 g // Protein 2.1 g // Fibre 5.8 g // Fat 17.0 g // Saturated fat 2.4 g // Salt 1.2 g*

1. To make the dressing, combine the oil, red wine vinegar, balsamic vinegar, mustard, salt, stevia liquid, and pepper to taste in a small bowl.

2. Holding half an avocado in your palm, insert the tip of a tablespoon into the narrow end of the fruit and up between the fruit and skin so that the flesh is removed in one piece. Put it on a board and repeat with the other halves, then cut diagonally into 5-mm/¼-inch slices. Halve the onion slices.

3. Arrange the avocado slices and cherry tomatoes on a serving platter and scatter over the onion pieces. Spoon over the dressing and scatter the basil leaves on top. Serve immediately.

*Serves: 4 // Preparation time: 10 minutes // Cooking time: None*

2 ripe avocados, halved and stoned
1 small red onion, thinly sliced
12 cherry tomatoes, halved
handful of fresh basil leaves

**Dressing**
2 tbsp extra virgin olive oil
1½ tsp red wine vinegar
1 tsp balsamic vinegar
1 tsp Dijon mustard
1 tsp salt
1 drop of stevia liquid
pepper

This salad is high in fat (albeit the healthy monounsaturated type) so if you are watching your weight, serve it with a low-fat accompaniment to bring down the overall calorie count of the meal.

*Tip //*

1
2
3

# Red cabbage, orange and walnut coleslaw

A refreshing and tangy salad you'll want to make time and again to go with steak, roast chicken or anything else you fancy.

*Calories 148 // Carbohydrates 10.2 g // Sugars 4.7 g // Protein 2.7 g // Fibre 3.0 g // Fat 11.7 g // Saturated fat 1.0 g // Salt 1.2 g*

100 g/3½ oz red cabbage, thinly shredded
100 g/3½ oz white cabbage, thinly shredded
1 small red onion, thinly sliced
1 orange
40 g/1½ oz walnut pieces
handful of fresh coriander leaves

**Dressing**
1½ tbsp walnut oil
2 tsp white wine vinegar
1 tsp Dijon mustard
1 drop of stevia liquid
½ tsp salt
pepper

1. Tip the red cabbage and white cabbage into a serving bowl.

2. Halve the onion slices and add to the bowl.

3. Using a sharp knife, cut a slice from the top and the bottom of the orange. Remove the peel and white pith by cutting downwards, following the shape of the fruit as closely as possible. Working over a small bowl to catch any juice, cut between the flesh and the membrane of each segment and ease out the flesh. Slice each segment in half. Squeeze the membrane over a small bowl to extract the juice. Add the orange pieces to the serving bowl.

4. To make the dressing, add the oil, vinegar, mustard, stevia liquid, salt, and pepper to taste to the bowl with the orange juice and whisk together.

5. Stir the dressing, walnut pieces and coriander leaves into the serving bowl. Serve immediately.

*Serves: 4 // Preparation time: 15 minutes // Cooking time: None*

Cabbage has a low GI rating of around 15 and is therefore an ideal vegetable to include in your diet. The addition of oil-rich walnuts and walnut oil helps slow down the rate at which the food is absorbed into your bloodstream.

*Tip //*

1
3
4

# Fresh Caribbean salsa

Here is a salad to perk up your taste buds – try serving it with ham or spicy chicken, or stir some prawns or crab into it for a simple starter.

*Calories 74 // Carbohydrates 10.0 g // Sugars 5.5 g // Protein 1.2 g // Fibre 1.7 g // Fat 3.7 g // Saturated fat 0.2 g // Salt 0.2 g*

1 large yellow pepper, deseeded and cut into 1-cm/½-inch dice
½ cucumber, quartered, deseeded and cut into 1-cm/½-inch dice
2 slices fresh pineapple, about 15-mm/⅝ inch thick, chopped
2 spring onions, chopped
2 fresh red chillies, deseeded and finely chopped
handful of fresh coriander leaves, to garnish

**Dressing**
juice of 1 lime
1 tsp jerk seasoning
1 tbsp extra virgin rapeseed oil

1. Put the yellow pepper, cucumber, pineapple, spring onions and chillies into a serving bowl.

2. To make the dressing, combine the lime juice, jerk seasoning and oil in a small bowl.

3. Pour the dressing over the salad and stir thoroughly. Scatter the coriander leaves over the top and serve immediately.

*Serves: 4 // Preparation time: 15 minutes // Cooking time: None*

Regular consumption of (unpeeled) cucumber is excellent for anyone who has hypertension, which can lead to heart disease. This is because it is high in potassium, which can significantly lower blood pressure.

*Tip //*

# Cannellini bean dip with crudités

If you're a fan of hummus, try this equally enjoyable dip. Served with crunchy crudités and strips of pitta, it makes a good starter or snack.

*Calories 184 // Carbohydrates 19.0 g // Sugars 2.1 g // Protein 6.3 g // Fibre 4.7 g // Fat 8.6 g // Saturated fat 1.2 g // Salt 1.3 g*

*Tip //*

These small white beans are particularly high in resistant starch, as well as being high in both soluble and insoluble fibre, so this dip is one of the best snacks you can eat to help control blood sugars.

1 wholemeal pitta bread
⅓ cucumber, quartered lengthways, deseeded and cut into sticks
3 celery sticks, halved lengthways and cut into sticks
4 radishes, quartered

**Dip**

400 g/14 oz canned cannellini beans in water, drained and rinsed
3 garlic cloves, crushed
juice of ½ lemon
2½ tbsp olive oil
1 tsp salt
pepper

1. To make the dip, tip the beans into the bowl of a food processor. Add the garlic, lemon juice, oil, salt, and pepper to taste. Pulse for 20 seconds, or until a thick paste forms. Alternatively, place the ingredients in a mixing bowl and beat thoroughly with a wooden spoon to combine. Add a little water if the mixture is too stiff. Transfer to a small bowl.

2. Preheat the grill to medium and lightly toast the pitta bread. Cut into eight strips.

3. Place the bowl of dip in the centre of a plate, surrounded by the crudités and pitta bread strips. Serve immediately.

*Serves: 4 // Preparation time: 15 minutes // Cooking time: 5 minutes*

1
1
1

2

3

6

# Mixed vegetable crisps

These crisps – made with a combination of root vegetables – are even more delicious than the higher-GI ones you can buy at the supermarket.

*Calories 128 // Carbohydrates 19.2 g // Sugars 5.4 g // Protein 1.8 g // Fibre 4.1 g // Fat 5.2 g // Saturated fat 0.7 g // Salt 1.3 g*

100 g/3½ oz carrots
100 g/3½ oz parsnips
100 g/3½ oz sweet potatoes
100 g/3½ oz beetroot
125 g/4½ oz waxy potatoes, such as Charlotte or Pink Fir Apple, unpeeled
1½ tbsp olive oil
1 tsp salt
½ tsp sweet paprika
pepper

1. Preheat the oven to 190°C/375°F/Gas Mark 5. Line three baking trays with baking paper.

2. Thinly slice the carrots, parsnips, sweet potatoes, beetroot and potatoes. (It is a good idea to use a mandoline or a food processor to do this so that you can get the slices nice and thin.)

3. Dry the vegetable slices between sheets of thick kitchen paper.

4. Combine the oil with the salt, paprika, and pepper to taste in a small bowl. Put all the vegetables except the beetroot into a large bowl and add most of the oil mixture – toss thoroughly to combine.

5. Put the beetroot into a separate bowl with the remaining oil mixture and toss well. (If you toss the beetroot with the other vegetables their colour will bleed.)

6. Arrange the vegetable slices on the prepared baking trays, keeping the beetroot separate. Bake in the centre of the preheated oven for 10 minutes, then turn the vegetables with a spatula and bake for a further 5–10 minutes, or until they are golden and cooked through.

7. Transfer to wire racks and leave to cool until crisp. Toss all the vegetable crisps to combine before transferring to a bowl to serve.

*Serves: 4 // Preparation time: 15–20 minutes // Cooking time: 15–20 minutes, plus cooling*

Baking or roasting root vegetables helps to increase their levels of resistant starch.

*Tip //*

# Home-made cashew nut butter

Making your own nut butter is easy and, unlike many shop-bought nut butters, this one is free of added sugar.

*Calories 153 // Carbohydrates 8.4 g // Sugars 1.6 g // Protein 5.0 g // Fibre 0.9 g // Fat 12.0 g // Saturated fat 2.1 g // Salt 0.3 g*

500 g/1 lb 2 oz whole raw cashew nuts
1 tsp salt
½ tsp vanilla extract

1. Preheat the oven to 140°C/275°F/Gas Mark 1. Tip the nuts into the bowl of a food processor with the salt. Grind to small pieces. Whizz, taking a rest every minute or so, until the nuts warm up and begin to release their oils.

2. Continue processing until a creamy, silky nut butter forms. Add the vanilla extract and process once more to combine.

3. Wash two 225-g/8-oz lidded jars and rinse thoroughly, then dry with a clean tea towel or kitchen paper. Put the jars on a baking tray and heat in the preheated oven for 20 minutes. Sterilize the lids by boiling them in water for 5 minutes, then dry them on kitchen paper.

4. Using a clean spoon, fill the jars with the nut butter and cover with the lids. Store in the refrigerator to preserve the unsaturated oils in the butter. Remove from the refrigerator 1 hour before using so the butter will spread more easily. It will keep in the refrigerator for several weeks.

*Makes: 18 servings (each 25 g / 1 oz / 1 heaped tbsp) // Preparation time: 15 minutes // Cooking time: 20 minutes (to sterilize jars)*

Buy whole cashew nuts for this recipe (rather than cashew nut pieces) as they will have retained more of their valuable unsaturated fats, and don't use roasted nuts or the recipe won't work.

*Tip //*

# Fruit, nut and seed trail mix

This trail mix is lower in sugars than many shop-bought mixes. It's worth keeping a small pot with you to nibble on during the day.

*Calories 132 // Carbohydrates 7.5 g // Sugars 3.0 g // Protein 4.5 g // Fibre 2.4 g // Fat 10.4 g // Saturated fat 1.5 g // Salt Trace*

225 g/8 oz almonds
3 tbsp pine nuts
3 tbsp pumpkin seeds
3 tbsp sunflower seeds
40 g/1½ oz dried banana chips
40 g/1½ oz dates, stoned and roughly chopped
2 tbsp oat bran
½ tsp ground mixed spice
1 small egg white

1. Preheat the oven to 200°C/400°F/Gas Mark 6. Combine the almonds, pine nuts, pumpkin and sunflower seeds, banana chips, dates, oat bran and mixed spice in a large bowl and mix well.

2. Lightly beat the egg white with a fork in a small bowl, then add to the nut mixture in the bowl, stirring to coat all the ingredients evenly.

3. Spread the mixture out in a single layer on a large baking sheet. Bake in the preheated oven for 8–10 minutes, or until crisp and lightly browned.

4. Leave to cool completely before serving. The trail mix will keep for up to 5 days stored in an airtight container.

*Makes: 17 servings (each 25 g/1 oz) // Preparation time: 10 minutes // Cooking time: 8–10 minutes, plus cooling*

Eating just a small handful of almonds a day provides a host of health benefits. Almonds have been shown to aid weight loss and reduce abdominal fat. They can also help to prevent hunger and moderate blood glucose levels in diabetics.

*Tip //*

1
2
3

# Simple snacks

The ideal snack is one that has a good balance of carbohydrates and protein; contains a little – but not too much – fat (unless it is mostly healthy monounsaturated or Omega-3 fats); contains some vitamins and minerals; has a good fibre content; and is low in sugar. Here are some ideas that will all contribute to a healthy diet and help to keep your blood sugars on an even keel until your next meal, without offering too many calories. You can freely add salad leaves, cucumber, radish and fresh herbs to your choice of snack.

*TIP: Try to balance your choice of snack with what you ate at the previous meal and will be eating at the next one. For example, if your next meal will be high in fresh vegetables, it is fine if your snack is just cheese and a biscuit.*

1 hard-boiled egg with a dark rye crispbread
*(Calories 114 / Carbohydrates 6.7 g)*

*

1 slice reduced-salt ham spread with a little Dijon mustard and rolled up in a lettuce leaf
*(Calories 36 / Carbohydrates 1.0 g)*

*

Small handful (20 g/¾ oz) of almonds
*(Calories 115 / Carbohydrates 4.3 g)*

*

Small handful of any seeds with 2 ready-to-eat dried apricots
*(Calories 101 / Carbohydrates 6.0 g)*

*

2-cm/¾-inch square reduced-fat Cheddar cheese with 1 rough oatcake and a cherry tomato
*(Calories 109 / Carbohydrates 7.1 g)*

*

1 tbsp hummus with ½ wholemeal pitta bread
*(Calories 102 / Carbohydrates 16.4 g)*

*

1 tbsp peanut or cashew nut butter on 1 celery stick
*(Calories 100 / Carbohydrates 4.6g)*

*

1 tbsp guacamole with 15 g/½ oz (½ slice) dark rye bread
*(Calories 113 / Carbohydrates 7.2 g)*

*

1 carrot cut into batons and served with 45 g/1½ oz tzatziki
*(Calories 84 / Carbohydrates 7.8 g)*

*

125 g/4½ oz natural live yogurt with 1 tbsp milled flaxseed and 1 tsp agave nectar
*(Calories 133 / Carbohydrates 13.1 g)*

*

½ wholemeal English muffin with 1 tbsp extra-light cream cheese and tomato slices
*(Calories 97 / Carbohydrates 14.8 g)*

*

Small handful (25 g/1 oz) of *Fruit, nut and seed trail mix* (see page 130)
*(Calories 132 / Carbohydrates 7.5 g)*

# Baking and desserts

1
2
5

# Pumpernickel bread

This unusual recipe for a dark rye loaf contains polenta, potatoes and cocoa! The result is a rich, dark and flavoursome bread.

*Calories 135 // Carbohydrates 27.8 g // Sugars 3.7 g // Protein 5.0 g // Fibre 6.2 g // Fat 1.5 g // Saturated fat 0.2 g // Salt 0.4 g*

75 g/2¾ oz quick-cook polenta
300 ml/10 fl oz cold water
60 g/2¼ oz molasses sugar
1 tbsp light olive oil
1½ tsp salt
2 tsp caraway seeds
1 tbsp cocoa powder
225 g/8 oz cold or lukewarm mashed potatoes
400 g/14 oz dark rye flour
150 g/5½ oz plain wholemeal flour, plus extra for sprinkling
15 g/½ oz easy-blend dried yeast
100 ml/3½ fl oz lukewarm water
cooking spray, for oiling

1. Put the polenta into a saucepan with the cold water and cook over a low heat, stirring constantly, for 5 minutes, or until it has thickened to a porridge-like consistency. Remove from the heat and add the sugar, oil, salt, caraway seeds and cocoa powder. Stir to combine and leave to cool slightly.

2. Stir in the mashed potatoes, then add in the rye flour, wholemeal flour, yeast and lukewarm water and knead for 10 minutes, or until the dough is smooth and pliable.

3. Spray a large bowl with cooking spray and put the dough in the bowl. Cover with a clean tea towel and leave to stand in a warm place for around 45 minutes, or until doubled in size.

4. Meanwhile, preheat the oven to 190°C/375°F/ Gas Mark 5. Spray a 1-kg/2 lb 4-oz loaf tin with cooking spray.

5. Put the dough into the prepared tin, shaping it to fit. Make a few diagonal cuts along the top and sprinkle with a little wholemeal flour. Bake in the preheated oven for 1 hour, or until the loaf sounds hollow when tapped on the base. Leave to cool in the tin for 10 minutes, then transfer to a wire rack to cool completely.

*Makes: 20 slices // Preparation time: 25–30 minutes, plus rising // Cooking time: 1 hr 10 mins, plus cooling*

The dark rye flour and cocoa bring the glycaemic load of this bread right down so that you can enjoy a slice knowing that your blood sugars are not going to spike suddenly.

*Tip //*

# Cheese and herb scones

These delicious cheese scones are an excellent mid-morning treat, or you could try one instead of bread with a lunchtime ham salad.

*Calories 213 // Carbohydrates 32.0 g // Sugars 1.1 g // Protein 7.9 g // Fibre 2.8 g // Fat 6.4 g // Saturated fat 2.9 g // Salt 1.2 g*

cooking spray, for oiling
335 g/11¾ oz self-raising wholemeal flour
335 g/11¾ oz self-raising white flour, plus extra for dusting
½ tsp baking powder
¼ tsp salt
75 g/2¾ oz baking margarine (from a block), chopped
100 g/3½ oz reduced-fat mature Cheddar cheese, finely grated
1½ tbsp finely snipped fresh chives
1 tbsp finely chopped fresh rosemary leaves
300 ml/10 fl oz semi-skimmed milk
30 g/1 oz freshly grated Parmesan cheese

1. Preheat the oven to 220°C/425°F/Gas Mark 7. Spray a large baking tray with cooking spray.

2. Sift the wholemeal flour, white flour, baking powder and salt into a mixing bowl, tipping in any bran left in the sieve, and stir to combine. Add the margarine and rub it into the flour with your fingertips until the mixture resembles breadcrumbs. Stir in the Cheddar cheese, chives and rosemary.

3. Make a well in the centre of the dry ingredients and pour in all but 2 tablespoons of the milk, stirring with a metal spatula until a dough begins to form, then finish the process using your hands. If necessary, add a little more milk or water (you need only enough to form a stiff dough).

4. Turn out onto a lightly floured work surface and knead gently to form a smooth dough. Add more flour to the work surface and the rolling pin if necessary, then roll out the dough to a thickness of 2 cm/¾ inch. Cut out 16 scones with a 7.5-cm/3-inch round cutter

5. Put the scones on the prepared tray, evenly spaced out. Brush the tops with the remaining milk, then sprinkle over the Parmesan cheese. Bake in the preheated oven for 15–20 minutes, or until the scones are golden and cooked through, and they sound hollow when tapped on the base. Serve warm or cold. The scones can be frozen for up to 1 month.

*Makes: 16 // Preparation time: 20–25 minutes // Cooking time: 15–20 minutes, plus cooling*

You can use wholemeal spelt flour instead of the wholemeal self-raising flour for a nutty change – add 2 teaspoons of baking powder and ½ teaspoon of salt to the recipe to turn your spelt flour into self-raising flour.

*Tip //*

2

2

4

# Nut and seed bars

The sugar content of many shop-bought fruit, nut and seed bars is often very high. These bars bring the sugar down to an acceptable level.

*Calories 213 // Carbohydrates 21.7 g // Sugars 6.8 g // Protein 6.2 g // Fibre 4g // Fat 12.0 g // Saturated fat 1.8 g // Salt 0.3 g*

4 tbsp groundnut oil
3 tbsp cashew nut butter
1 tbsp maple syrup
2 tbsp stevia granules
50 g/1¾ oz milled flaxseed
250 g/9 oz unsweetened apple sauce
1 tsp vanilla extract
240 g/8½ oz rolled oats
115 g/4 oz ready-to-eat dried apricots, chopped
50 g/1¾ oz pumpkin seeds
50 g/1¾ oz sunflower seeds
½ tsp ground cinnamon
¼ tsp salt

1. Preheat the oven to 170°C/340°F/Gas Mark 3–4. Line a 24 x 16-cm/9½ x 6¼-inch shallow baking tin with baking paper.

2. Put the oil, cashew nut butter, maple syrup and stevia granules in a small saucepan and heat gently, stirring constantly, until well combined and the nut butter is melted.

3. Remove from the heat, add the flaxseed, apple sauce and vanilla extract and combine thoroughly.

4. Mix together the oats, dried apricots, pumpkin seeds, sunflower seeds, cinnamon and salt in a large mixing bowl. Spoon the nut butter mixture into the bowl and stir until well combined.

5. Spoon the mixture into the prepared tin, pressing it down and out into the corners with your fingers until the tin is evenly filled.

6. Bake in the preheated oven for 40 minutes, or until the top is golden. Leave to cool in the tin for 5 minutes, then remove from the tin and cut into 15 bars. Transfer to a wire rack to cool completely. Store in an airtight container for up to 1 week.

*Makes: 15 // Preparation time: 20 minutes // Cooking time: 45 minutes, plus cooling*

The seed selection in the bars is rich in unsaturated fats – including Omega-3s and monounsaturates – as well as being high in soluble and insoluble fibre and resistant starch.

*Tip //*

# Oat, blueberry and nut cookies

Using stevia in this recipe reduces the total sugar content right down so that you can enjoy a real fruit and nut cookie without guilt!

*Calories 145 // Carbohydrates 17.0 g // Sugars 1.4 g // Protein 3.8 g // Fibre 2.4 g // Fat 7.3 g // Saturated fat 1.4 g // Salt 0.2 g*

cooking spray, for oiling
4 tbsp groundnut oil
60 g/2¼ oz baking margarine (from a block), at room temperature
15 g/½ oz stevia granules
2 tbsp clear honey
1 large egg
1 tsp vanilla extract
150 g/5½ oz plain wholemeal flour or spelt flour
100 g/3½ oz plain white flour
150 g/5½ oz rolled oats
125 g/4½ oz medium oatmeal
1 tsp bicarbonate of soda
¼ tsp salt
200 g/7 oz blueberries
80 g/2¾ oz chopped hazelnuts

1. Preheat the oven to 180°C/350°F/Gas Mark 4. Spray a large baking tray with cooking spray.

2. In a large mixing bowl, beat together the oil, margarine, stevia granules and honey until creamy, then beat in the egg and vanilla extract with 1 tablespoon of the flour.

3. In a separate bowl, combine the wholemeal flour, white flour, oats, oatmeal, bicarbonate of soda and salt. Add the blueberries and hazelnuts and gently stir to combine (you don't want the blueberries to break up at this stage).

4. Stir the flour mixture into the oil mixture until thoroughly combined. Drop 25 spoonfuls of the mixture onto the prepared baking tray.

5. Bake the cookies in the preheated oven for about 15 minutes, until set around the edges and golden but still with some 'give' in the centre if you push with your thumb.

6. Using a spatula, transfer the cookies to a wire rack to cool completely. Store in an airtight container for up to 1 week.

*Makes: 25 // Preparation time: 20–25 minutes // Cooking time: 15 minutes, plus cooling*

Studies on blueberries have shown that they can help with blood sugar control because of the plant compounds (phenols) that they contain.

*Tip //*

2
3
4

2

3

4

# Pumpkin pie muffins

If you love pumpkin pie, the good news is that you can enjoy all those lovely flavours in a healthy low-fat, low-saturates muffin.

*Calories 225 // Carbohydrates 42.0 g // Sugars 7.5 g // Protein 7.6 g // Fibre 5.2 g // Fat 4.1 g // Saturated fat 0.6 g // Salt 0.8 g*

330 g/11½ oz plain wholemeal flour
125 g/4½ oz oatmeal
1¼ tsp baking powder
¾ tsp bicarbonate of soda
¼ tsp salt
2 tsp ground mixed spice
65 g/2¼ oz molasses sugar
1 tbsp stevia granules
2 egg whites
2 tsp vanilla extract
275 g/9¾ oz cooked pumpkin flesh (about 325 g/11½ oz uncooked weight), mashed until smooth
1½ tbsp groundnut oil
100 g/3½ oz unsweetened apple sauce
250 ml/9 fl oz unsweetened vanilla almond milk

1. Preheat the oven to 180°C/350°F/Gas Mark 4. Line ten holes in a 12-hole muffin tin with paper cases.

2. Put the flour, oatmeal, baking powder, bicarbonate of soda, salt and mixed spice into a large bowl and mix to combine thoroughly.

3. Beat together the sugar, stevia granules, egg whites and vanilla extract in a mixing bowl, then beat in the mashed pumpkin, oil, apple sauce and almond milk. Add the flour mixture and beat until just mixed.

4. Divide the mixture between the paper cases. Bake in the preheated oven for 25 minutes, or until a skewer inserted into the centre of a muffin comes out clean.

5. Leave the muffins to cool in the tin until cool enough to handle, then transfer to a wire rack to cool completely. They are best eaten within 24 hours but will store for a little longer, and will freeze for up to 1 month.

*Makes: 10 // Preparation time: 20–25 minutes // Cooking time: 25 minutes, plus cooling*

*Tip //*

To cook the pumpkin, simply put the prepared pumpkin chunks in a microwaveable bowl with a little water and cook in the microwave at 850 watts for 8 minutes, or until tender. The pumpkin needs to be soft enough to mash easily.

# Fitting your favourite foods into your diet

There is no food that must be completely banned from your diet, even if you are diabetic. What ultimately matters is the overall quality of your diet, and that you monitor your carbohydrate intake, especially if you are using supplementary insulin. It is always sensible to make sure that at each meal or snack occasion you balance what you eat so that the total glycaemic load of the meal is acceptable.

To do this is simple enough. For example, if your favourite food happens to be a high-sugar, low-fibre item, such as a pack of sweets, then limit how much you eat and add a high-protein/moderate-fat item to the snack to bring down its glycaemic load – in this case, you might add a few nuts. This trick also has the benefit of keeping you feeling full for longer and avoiding the urge to dip into the sweet pack later on. To give another example, if you love a plate of white pasta, make sure the topping is a high-protein one with plenty of fibre – for example, tuna and broccoli with peas and tomato sauce.

If you are watching your weight, there are several things you can do to make sure that your favourite foods can be included in your diet without compromising your weight loss or weight maintenance.

* Eat mindfully. Each time you eat a 'treat' food or one that you know is very high in calories, try to make sure that you really appreciate it, enjoy it and savour it. When it is finished, feel happy and move away from the food area and do something else that makes you happy.

* It helps to pay full attention to your food at every meal, chewing thoroughly and eating as slowly as you can. By paying attention to what you're doing, you can stop eating the moment you have had enough. This one simple trick can reduce your overall food intake more than you might imagine, so that you then have calories 'saved' for a treat or extra.

* Add one or two healthy elements into your favourite meal, if you can, to improve its nutritional profile. For example, if you have a plate of low-fibre white rice and lamb curry, add in high-fibre vegetables, such as spinach, broccoli, onions and tomatoes. This way you may also eat fewer calories and less fat as the vegetables bulk your meal out.

* Limit portion sizes of the foods that are less good for you – it really helps to eat from a smaller plate or dish, and, if cooking, to make a portion in the first place that is not too large, so there are no leftovers to go back for.

* See if you can find a lower-fat, lower-salt or lower-sugar version of your favourite food that is still acceptable to you. Most supermarkets stock healthier versions of cheese, yogurts, sauces, desserts, crisps, ready-meals and many more.